ALL ABOUT RADIATION

TO THE READER:

Scientology® is a religious philosophy containing pastoral counseling procedures intended to assist an individual to gain greater knowledge of self. The Mission of the Church of Scientology is a simple one—to help the individual achieve greater self-confidence and personal integrity, thereby enabling him to really trust and respect himself and his fellow man. The attainment of the benefits and goals of Scientology requires each individual's positive participation, as only through his own efforts can he achieve these.

This is part of the religious literature and works of the Founder of Scientology, L. Ron Hubbard. It is presented to the reader as part of the record of his personal research into Life, and should be construed only as a written report of such research and not as a statement of claims made by the Church or the author.

Scientology and its sub-study, Dianetics, as practiced by the Church, address only the spiritual side of Man. Although the Church, as are all churches, is free to engage in spiritual healing, it does not, as its primary goal is increased knowledge and personal integrity for all. For this reason, the Church does not wish to accept individuals who desire treatment of physical illness or insanity, but refers these to qualified specialists in other organizations who deal in these matters.

The Hubbard Electrometer is a religious artifact used in the Church confessional. It, in itself, does nothing, and is used by Ministers only, to assist parishioners in locating areas of spiritual distress or travail.

We hope the reading of this book is only the first stage of a personal voyage of discovery into the positive and effective religion of Scientology.

THE BOARD OF DIRECTORS

Church of Scientology

This book belongs to _____

Date _____

ALL ABOUT RADIATION

by
A NUCLEAR PHYSICIST
and
A MEDICAL DOCTOR

SCIENTOLOGY PUBLICATIONS ORGANIZATION

Published in
The United States of America
by
Church of Scientology of California
PUBLICATIONS ORGANIZATION UNITED STATES
4833 Fountain Avenue, East Annex
Los Angeles, California 90029

ISBN 0-88404-062-3

and in all other countries
by
SCIENTOLOGY PUBLICATIONS ORGANIZATION
(AOSH DK Publications Department ApS)
Jernbanegade 6, 1608 Copenhagen V
Denmark

ISBN 87-7336-029-5

The Church of Scientology of
California is a non-profit organization

Scientology is an Applied Religious Philosophy.
Dianetics® and Scientology® are registered names.

This book was written out of the proceedings of the
CONGRESS ON NUCLEAR RADIATION AND HEALTH
given at the Royal Empire Society Hall between April 12th and
15th, 1957 by the courtesy of
THE HUBBARD SCIENTOLOGY ORGANIZATION
68 Tottenham Court Road
London, W.1., England
and transcribed as requested by Members of Parliament
as furnished to them.

The E-Meter is not intended or effective for the diagnosis
treatment or prevention of any disease.

A Dianetics Publication.
Dianetics is the trademark of L. Ron Hubbard
in respect of his published works.

1979 Edition Produced & Released by
LRH Personal Compilations Bureau
In-Charge: Pat Brice
Research Chief: Ernie Ryan

DEDICATION

*To Sir Winston Churchill who could have
written and said it much better.*

*And to Dwight D. Eisenhower who could
solve it if he had a little more cooperation.*

The Authors.

"Man's inhumanity to man makes countless thousands mourn."

——Robert Burns.

All mail addressed to me shall be received by me. I am always willing to help. By my own creed, a being is only as valuable as he can serve others.

Any message addressed to me and sent to the address of the nearest Scientology church listed in the back of this book, will be forwarded to me directly.

L. Ron Hubbard

IMPORTANT NOTE

One of the biggest barriers to learning a new subject is its nomenclature, meaning the set of terms used to describe the things it deals with. A subject must have accurate labels which have exact meanings before it can be understood and communicated.

If I were to describe parts of the body as "thingamabobs" and "whatsernames," we would all be in a confusion, so the accurate naming of something is a very important part of any field.

A student comes along and starts to study something and has a terrible time of it. Why? Because he or she not only has a lot of new principles and methods to learn, but a whole new language as well. Unless the student understands this, unless he or she realizes that one has to "know the words before one can sing the tune," he or she is not going to get very far in any field of study or endeavor.

Now I am going to give you an important datum:

The only reason a person gives up a study or becomes confused or unable to learn is because he or she has gone past a word that was not understood.

The confusion or inability to grasp or learn comes AFTER a word that the person did not have defined and understood.

Have you ever had the experience of coming to the end of a page and realizing you didn't know what you had read? Well, somewhere earlier on that page you went past a word that you had no definition for.

Here's an example. "It was found that when the crepuscule arrived the children were quieter and when it was not present, they were much livelier." You see what happens. You think you don't understand the whole idea, but the inability to understand came entirely from the one word you could not define, *crepuscule* which means twilight or darkness.

This datum about not going past an undefined word is the most important fact in the whole subject of study. Every subject you have taken up and abandoned had its words which you failed to get defined.

Therefore, in studying Scientology be very, very certain you never go past a word you do not fully understand. If the material becomes confusing or you can't seem to grasp it, there will be a word just earlier that you have not understood. Don't go any further, but go back to BEFORE you got into trouble, find the misunderstood word and get it defined.

That is why we have a dictionary. It will not only be the new and unusual words that you will have to look up. Some commonly used words can be misdefined and so cause confusion. So don't depend on our dictionary alone.

Use a general English language dictionary as well for any non-Scientology word you do not understand when you are reading or studying.

Scientology words and their definitions are the gateway to a new look and understanding of life. Understanding them will help you live better, and will assist you along the road of truth that is Scientology.

CONTENTS

Book One

The Facts About The Atomic Bomb

by Medicus

Introduction

Are people generally aware of their responsibilities as individual members of the human race?

Man throughout known history has always been busy inventing—and using—bigger and better machines for the destruction of his fellows. Organized science which in the 20th Century has brought to everyone benefits with immeasurable possibilities for a happier and more creative life, has also produced a weapon which in a single ferocious explosion can destroy utterly even the largest city on earth. Some further possibilities of this appalling destructiveness, though not generally well-known, are of more importance, if possible, to mankind even than those commonly envisaged. Here is abundant evidence that atomic weapons do not cease destroying when their explosions are over. The radioactive products released into the atmosphere retain their radioactivity, in some cases for a number of years, falling slowly to earth as dust and affecting the air we breathe, even thousands of miles from the area of the explosion. The accumulation of sufficient of these substances, could within a short time render Earth barren of all life. The danger point is not as remote as wishful thinking would have it. Short of this final limit are possibilities, already almost probabilities, of slow degeneration, insidious illness and increasing sterility in all living things.

The intention of the writers in this book is to explain in language easily understood, the more important effects of atomic explosions, both short and long term, and to outline methods of protection and treatment of human beings, so far known to be of some value. They also wish to draw to the attention of everyone, as individual living and thinking beings, their responsibilities toward themselves, their families and friends, and their neighbors near and far in this context.

CHAPTER ONE

The Atomic Bomb

Let it be stated definitely at the outset that a thing understood is a thing less feared. Atomic energy in all its uses has been the subject of much mystery and secrecy. This is so partly because the peculiarly "atomic" radiations are imperceptible to human senses and partly on account of national security measures. Some clarity needs to be brought at once into the public attitude regarding atomic weapons and it is hoped that the following simple explanations, both of what man is facing and what he can do to help himself, may achieve this.

The so-called "nominal bomb" will be the main subject of description. This is roughly equivalent in power to 20,000 tons of conventional high explosive (T.N.T.) and is described therefore as a 20 kiloton (20 kt) bomb. The weapons used on Japan in 1945 were of this order of magnitude. The hydrogen, or thermonuclear, weapon differs in its effects from the above only in quantity not in quality. A brief reference will be made in a later paragraph to the important differences and the special dangers.

3

The mechanism of the bomb is basically simple and a slight understanding of it is useful to trace the development of its action. The explosive material is a pure mass of fissionable metal. A form of uranium (U235) and plutonium were the first such materials to be discovered. The only other fundamental constituent required is a source of neutrons (uncharged subatomic particles). Atoms of the metal can capture wandering neutrons. The nucleus of the atom thus augmented is unstable and immediately splits into two roughly equal halves which form the nuclei of lighter elements (the "fission products"). At the same time two neutrons are released for each one captured and each atom of metal split. These may escape from the bomb mass or may be captured by more atoms of metal. If the total mass is greater than a certain critical size, more neutrons are captured than escape and a chain reaction develops. It proceeds in a bomb at an enormous rate (10^{12} stages in one second) and at each stage, much energy is liberated. Much of it is in the form of heat and at the point of explosion, a temperature of a million degrees centigrade is produced almost instantaneously, rendering the air and the remains of the bomb incandescent. This is the fireball which radiates a tremendous flash of heat and light, and the very high pressure (½ a million tons/ sq. in.) suddenly created within it sets up the blast wave. Part of the energy is released at the same time as the highly penetrating invisible gamma rays. A large quantity of neutrons is, of course, also released and is the other important invisible component of the radiation. These last two factors are highly dangerous to life and constitute the one fundamental respect in which atomic explosions differ from the conventional.

The fireball, which is about 450 yards in diameter, expands and rises rapidly into the upper atmosphere to become the familiar mushroom-shaped cloud. The light flash lasts for an instant only, the heat radiation for, at most, half a second, and the blast passes in a single wave taking perhaps one second. Most of the gamma and neutron radiation has passed in a couple of seconds, but some continues for about a minute, in fact until the radioactive cloud has risen into the upper atmosphere out of range.

Of all the effects of an atomic explosion the most important by far is blast. This of course is nothing new. Anyone who has been involved in war has had plenty of experience of it. It will inevitably cause an enormous amount of material damage and was in fact, in Japan, responsible for 60% of the casualties.

The heat flash is the next most important causing, directly or indirectly, 25% of the casualties. The invisible nuclear radiations caused only 15% of the casualties. In terms of a single bomb explosion these are thus rather a minor consideration. They are, however, much feared partly on account of their very invisibility and have been the subject of much controversial discussion. Breaking the new effects down numerically in this fashion tends to impart a real sense of proportion on the matter.

The real danger to life on a planetary scale does not lie in these immediate radiations. Here is the point. The explosion of the bomb produces a considerable amount of breakdown products, called fission products, by the splitting of the atoms of uranium. These are all initially radioactive and contaminate the atmosphere, settling gradually to Earth as dust over a period of years. Some of the products retain their radioactivity for more than 20 years so that an accumulation is bound to occur. The explosion of bombs for any purpose, military or otherwise, even at quite long intervals, can only increase the general radioactivity of Earth and atmosphere towards the danger point.

There is, however, some reason to believe that at the present rate of test explosions, particularly since many of them involve hydrogen weapons, that *within six to ten years from now sufficient radioactivity will have accumulated as to be generally dangerous to health if not to life.*

On account of the slow subsidence of dust from the upper atmosphere the actual effect would probably be postponed although inevitable. It has also been suggested that the explosion of about one thousand H-bombs altogether might be enough to destroy all life on the planet. If this figure should be inaccurate by a factor as great as ten, the situation is one which demands the urgent attention of every human being.

One other matter remains for inclusion in these general considerations. The psychological effect of an atomic explosion is considerable and interesting. Any person suffering a sudden and severe shock tends to go into a temporary state of helpless apathy. The duration of this state and its intensity, however, do vary a great deal according the the basic mental stability of the persons concerned. The atomic explosion is an instantaneous and utterly overwhelming shock, of a magnitude hitherto unknown on Earth. It produces in surviving victims a state of apathy of extraordinary degree. It is stated that, after the Japanese incidents, for a full twenty minutes following the explosion, no attempt was made by anyone to do anything. The reader will perceive that this is likely to produce permanent effect on an individual's mentality. There is some evidence also that the invisible nuclear radiations already referred to can themselves directly affect the mind. The possibility of wholesale mental aberration resulting from either of these causes in atomic warfare is one which cannot be lightly ignored. The reader is invited to ponder on this.

CHAPTER TWO

Protection

Blast

The blast from an atomic weapon differs somewhat in character from that experienced with conventional high explosives. The latter type of explosion gives a very short sharp blow lasting not more than a hundredth of a second, followed by an opposite phase of suction lasting perhaps twice as long. It happens in practice that the suction phase does the most damage, i.e. walls tend to fall outwards. The nuclear bomb, in contrast, gives a positive push lasting about one second. That is to say, it resembles a very strong wind. Most of the damage is done during this positive phase of the blast wave. Walls and buildings are pushed away from the point of explosion. Here is in fact a definite resemblance to the type of damage caused by natural storms. The suction phase is relatively unimportant.

The range of the blast wave and the degrees of damage that might be expected will now be described briefly.

Ordinary houses would be completely collapsed to a range of one thousand yards from ground zero. (Ground zero is the term used to describe the point on the ground immediately beneath the bomb when it explodes.) Up to a mile from ground zero irreparable damage could be expected. At greater distances houses would be rendered uninhabitable until major repairs had been done (1½ miles) or first aid (2½ miles). More lightly constructed buildings would, of course, be severely damaged or destroyed at even greater distances, say, up to a mile and a half. Reinforced concrete on the other hand, would probably survive outside a 600-yard radius with no more than superficial damage.

A major problem arising from blast would be the tremendous amount of debris blocking streets. This did not arise particularly in Japan, since the houses were mostly wooden and were completely destroyed by fire. But in a Western city complete impassability would be likely for a distance of half a mile or more from ground zero. Severe hampering of fire fighting and rescue work would inevitably result.

As regards the effect of blast on personnel, there would be few direct casualties. Anyone close enough to the explosion to be killed by blast would be killed anyway by the other factors. However, many casualties would be expected due to collapsing buildings at various ranges.

Protection of personnel from blast can be achieved

to a degree by similar measures to those familiar in "conventional" warfare. Deep shelters and basements with several means of exit should be satisfactory against anything but a ground-level burst close by. The "Anderson" type shelter much used in the 1939-45 war, or a deep trench with a thick layer of earth on top, provides fair protection. No particularly new problem exists here. The difference between an atomic weapon and an H-bomb is a matter only of size.

The blast wave travels at about the speed of sound. That is to say, it does not arrive at a point a mile or two from the explosion centre for several seconds after the light flash. There is, therefore, time to dive for cover, and this gives a slight safety factor. By the same means some of the gamma radiation may be escaped, and in the case of a Hydrogen bomb, some of the heat as well.

The basic principles amount, therefore, to "Take cover if you can" and, where more time is available, "Go underground."

Heat

The heat flash radiating in straight lines outward from the fireball lasts in its full intensity for only a fraction of a second. On account of the short duration only the surfaces of objects are affected. At these surfaces, however, a temperature of several thousand degrees centigrade is reached, up to a range of ½-¾ mile.

10

Within this distance surfaces of granite are melted and, on humans exposed in the open, burns involving the whole skin thickness are to be expected with some internal damage and immediate death. Since the flash is brief and nonpenetrating, relatively slight protection is a considerable safeguard. Any person properly under cover, i.e. out of the direct path of the rays, would not be affected. Clothing, particularly if loose, woollen and of a light color, offers appreciable protection although the clothing itself might catch fire. Severe to moderate burns would be suffered up to 1½-2 miles and slight burns at a greater distance.

The risk of fires and resulting burns is, of course, great. Combustible materials like cloth, dry wood, paper, etc., may well be ignited up to a distance of 1½ miles. This can occur inside buildings if the heat flash can enter through windows, open doors, etc. A simple means of protection for brick buildings is obvious: any kind of white opaque screen or even simply whitewashing windows would confer an appreciable degree of safety.

Fires arising from other causes constitute an additional danger. Damage to gas mains, overturning of domestic heating equipment of any kind and scattering of burning debris are more familiar wartime phenomena and no less important here.

There is a peculiarity in the manner of healing of burns caused by atomic explosions. This is a pronounced tendency to form thick, knotted, overgrown scars, known as keloids, which are very disfiguring and may be crippling. They were observed in Japan, and may be the result of the action of burning plus radiation. Malnutrition and poor treatment do definitely contribute, however; these were pronounced factors in Hiroshima and Nagasaki. Treatment, once keloids have developed, lies in the field of plastic surgery.

Light flash

As previously described a tremendous flash of light radiates for an instant at the moment of explosion. Its intensity, as seen during tests in the Pacific from a distance of 18 miles, was several times greater than that of the sun. Anybody without protection for the eyes would be totally blinded at a distance of several miles but, on past experience, the sight can be expected to recover within a matter of hours. There is some evidence that superficial skin burns due to light flash rather than heat can also occur even a number of miles from ground zero. These are not serious but can be very unpleasant. They are probably due to the ultraviolet component of the light.

Radiation

Several types of nuclear radiation are released by atomic explosions. These are:—

Alpha particles—Helium nuclei, therefore relatively heavy and slow, penetrate a very short distance in air and are of no importance in this context.

Beta particles—Electrons travelling at nearly the speed of light, penetrating a few feet in air, also of no importance in this context.

(Radioactive fission products coming in closer contact with the body can cause considerable damage, however, by means of these radiations—see later.)

Gamma rays—These for practical purposes are X-rays. They are of the same nature as light but of much higher frequency. They have a range in air of about 1½ miles and are the principal cause of radiation disease in atomic warfare.

Neutrons—These electrically uncharged particles are also higher penetrating. They travel a mile or more in air and cause damage to the body. They have the additional property of inducing radioactivity in objects which they strike.

A description of the actual effects of these rays on the human body follows in the next chapter. Meanwhile the problem of protection from them must be considered.

The intensity of gamma rays falls off with increasing distance from the source according to the inverse square law: that is to say, at double the distance the intensity would be reduced to a quarter. This applies to bomb bursts and small sources of radiation but not where the distance is small compared with the dimensions of the radiating surface. They are absorbed to some extent by air which, of course, limits their range, and by mist, fog or smoke rather more effectively. Their intensity is reduced by half by the following thicknesses of common protective substances approximately:—

Lead	1"	Concrete	5"
Steel	1½"	Earth	8"
	Water	11"	

These figures would be of some value in estimating the effectiveness of various sheltering constructions. The "Anderson" type shelter already referred to would reduce immediate radiation danger at moderate ranges very considerably. However, the thicker and heavier the protection, the better. The radiation from a burst only lasts a few seconds with a much smaller amount over a longer period. This last can, therefore, be escaped, together with the blast, if cover is taken at once, when the light flash is seen.

CHAPTER THREE

Nuclear Radiation

The effects of radiations depend basically on their property of rendering atoms in their path electrically charged. This is called ionization. The immediate result in the molecules, of which the ionized atoms are part, is increased chemical activity and a tendency to break up. Thus the living structure of the cell is altered or destroyed, and poisonous waste products may be formed. These changes, if on a sufficiently large scale, and in vital organs, can cause the death of the whole body.

The ionizing power of radiation depends on its energy. Alpha and beta particles are far more effective than gamma rays, but fortunately have very little penetrating power. Neutrons have quite high ionizing power, and penetrate easily as well. Dosages of radiation are measured in terms of total ionization, the unit being the "roentgen" (r). It is difficult to gain any subjective appreciation of what is meant by a dose of say 500 r, but the following observations give some idea:—

The lethal dose for a human being, if received

uniformly over the whole body, is about 750 r. That is to say, that such a dose could be expected to kill 100% of persons exposed to it, and is called an LD100 dose. It would be received by a person standing in the open at about 800 yards from ground zero in the case of a nominal bomb blast. An amount of 450 r, such as would be received up to 1,300 yards or so, would kill about 50% of persons exposed; it is thus an LD50 dose. Less than 200 r is not ordinarily fatal, unless the victim is already weakened from some other cause, or has received burns or blast injury as well.

About 50% of people exposed to a single dose of 200 r, however, could become quite ill, and might take anything up to three months to recover. 100 r produces about 10% sickness only, and less than 50 r in one dose can be taken as relatively harmless, provided there is no further exposure for many weeks, at least.

It will be obvious from the above that a good deal of individual variation occurs, but beyond the observation that the very young, the old, and the ill are more sensitive than normal, nothing is known of the reasons for the variations.

Much greater amounts of radiation than the above can be tolerated, if directed to specific parts of the body only, as for example in radiotherapy for cancer. On the other hand, much smaller doses, delivered to the whole body, do produce some ill effects, and furthermore, accumulate over a period of time. The sensitivity of human tissues decreases in this order: lymphatic tissue, testis, bone marrow (blood forming tissue), epithelium (lining) of the stomach and intestines, ovary. Brain and muscle are the least sensitive of all, and other tissues fall in between the two ranges. 1000 r to brain only is not lethal. On the other hand, 0.2 r per day over a period has been known to depress blood formation in workers with X-rays. The maximum safe continuous rate of irradiation for such people is now considered to be about 0.1 per day for five days a week. While a total dose accumulated over a long period is not as dangerous as the same dose given in a short time, radiation effects do nevertheless accumulate. In actual fact 60 r spread over three weeks is no more effective than 20 r as a single rapid dose. Nevertheless the expectation of life for radiologists, as observed in the U.S.A., is about five years less than that for others, and the incidence of leukemia in this group may be as high as ten times that in the whole population.

Death from irradiation may occur from several immediate causes, according to the dose received. Huge doses of many thousands of roentgen cause death from brain damage within a few hours. Death from an LD100 is usual due to destruction of the intestines and occurs in about 7-10 days. Smaller doses such as an LD50 may produce the same effect, or the victim may die from failure of blood manufacture in 4-6 weeks or so. If this period is survived recovery normally occurs, though the chronic risks remain, even with very small doses. Thus a number of victims can be expected to die after years from, for example, leukemia.

The general pattern of radiation disease from a rapid exposure is as follows:—The primary symptoms . . . nausea, diarrhea and particularly vomiting appear in 2-24 hours, and may last 2-14 days or so. Secondary symptoms . . . fever, bleeding under the skin and from orifices, loss of hair and more diarrhea appear after an interval of some few days up to several weeks. The earlier the onset of symptoms of either type, and the longer they last, the worse is the outlook for the patient, and an indication is thereby given of the dose received. Loss of hair and bleeding in the first week are the gravest signs; death is certain.

Most of the available data regarding the biological effects of radiation has been derived from observations made in Japan, during, and since 1945 supplemented by a growing body of evidence from animal experiments. Owing to the obvious impossibility of direct research on human beings, however, the picture is still far from complete.

CHAPTER FOUR

The Hydrogen Bomb

The H-bomb or thermonuclear weapon will now be described briefly. The explosion is a three-stage process:

1. An "ordinary" atom bomb serves as a "trigger".
2. The high temperature it produces makes possible the fusion of atoms of two rare forms of the element hydrogen. This reaction liberates more energy, and in particular yields large quantities of neutrons of much higher speeds than occur in the first stage.
3. These produce fission of the common and normally stable atoms of uranium 238. Large quantities of this can be used, as the casing of the bomb for example, and the power of the bomb is increased simply by adding more of it.

The power is expressed in terms of equivalence to millions of tons of T.N.T. (megatons). Weapons of up to 40 or more megatons have been tested, but the following descriptions will refer to a 10 megaton bomb exploded at ground level.

The actual fireball produced by this appalling contrivance is some three miles in diameter (cf. 450 yards for a nominal bomb), and the crater, one mile across. Up to a distance of 3 or 4 miles from ground zero total destruction could be expected; up to 15 miles severe damage from the blast; lighter damage up to 20 miles would occur. The blast effect at 15 miles has been calculated as equivalent to a 1,000 m.p.h. wind. Any of the largest cities in the world would thus suffer virtual annihilation from just one bomb.

The fire risk is equally terrifying. Persons exposed in the open 4 miles away would receive fatal burns; 8 miles away very severe burns; and up to 20 miles away progressively slighter burns. Fires would occur as much as 15 miles from ground zero. The heat "flash" from the bomb lasts from 10-30 seconds—much longer than from a nominal bomb. So much of it could be escaped at moderate ranges by taking cover.

The immediate radiation or "gamma flash" is of no importance since its range is so much less than that of the other effects. The H-bomb may produce, however, two tons or more of fission products compared with the five pounds yield of the nominal bomb. Residual radiation, therefore becomes of very great importance with this weapon, and will be discussed at some length in the next chapter.

CHAPTER FIVE

Problems of Delayed Radiation

The direct radiation from the radioactive cloud produced by an atomic explosion is effective for about a minute only—until the cloud has risen into the upper air. Radiations continue to be emitted from it, however, with decreasing intensity. Radioactive substances "decay" at varying rates, which average out for the fission products of the bomb thus:

For any given rate of radiation or dosage at time 1 hour after the explosion, the rate after

> 7 hours will be 1/10th
> 2 days will be 1/100th
> 2 weeks will be 1/1,000th
> 3 months will be 1/10,000th

The fine particles of the cloud take a long time to settle back to earth. When eventually they do settle the remaining radioactivity is negligible. There is, therefore, little obvious hazard from "fallout" due to an explosion taking place in the air. This applies to a nominal bomb which would probably be exploded at a height of about 1,000 feet, to obtain the maximum blast effect. Some localized neutron-induced surface radioactivity would occur but would be well decayed by the time rescue operations reached the area.

The H-bomb, by contrast, provides a very adequate blast for any conceivable purpose even if exploded at ground level. In this case, in addition to the fission products themselves, large quantities of earth and water are vaporized and rendered highly radioactive. The resulting particles settle much more quickly than the original bomb products. In a test at Bikini, using a 14 megaton bomb, an area of over 200 miles long and 40 miles wide, in a down-wind direction, was heavily contaminated. This is equal to a large part of southern England, whence the menace to a small country can be broadly appreciated.

Most of the "fallout" is deposited within 100 miles of ground zero, but enough to be dangerous is carried to much greater distances. The total doses of radiation that would have been received by a person in the open in the first 3 hours after this incident, at various distances, have been estimated as follows:

At   5 miles from ground zero . . . . . . 5000 r
At 105 miles from ground zero . . . . . . 2000 r
At 160 miles from ground zero . . . . . .   500 r
At 190 miles from ground zero . . . . . .   300 r

and the fallout decays in the manner described above. Under substantial cover the dose rate for most of the affected area would be so reduced as to be safe as regards life at least. Basements or slit trench shelters with a three foot covering of earth afford the best protection, and within them, only about 1/300th of the above doses would have been received. For lack of these a ground-floor room as far as possible from outside walls is fairly effective.

The amounts of radiation which can be tolerated by a human being, during various periods of time, are still a subject of controversy. A single dose of 50 r produces no observable effect, and therefore might be regarded as permissible during one day, provided there was no further exposure for several weeks. Under emergency conditions, the following figures have been suggested as safety limits:

50 r in 1 day.
25 r daily for 3 or 4 days.
5 r daily for 2 to 3 weeks.

A number of instruments exist for measuring dose rates in an area, or total dose received during a period of exposure. Civil defense personnel are equipped with these and would thus, by working in shifts, be able to carry out rescue and decontamination operations with minimum danger.

The basic precaution against "fallout" is thus to remain under cover, the most solid cover possible, for 48 hours after an incident. With the aid of the instruments, populations can then be advised when it has become definitely safe to emerge.

23

Anyone who for any reason has to be in the open when there is risk of contamination should use close fitting clothing including headgear, scarf, gloves and boots to exclude dust as completely as possible. In addition, any possibilities of inhaling radioactive dust must also be guarded against. Any antigas respirator, or a simple smog mask is effective, and in an emergency even a handkerchief tied round the face would do.

Decontamination

Objects contaminated by radioactive dust or water eventually become safe simply by natural decay of the radioactivity. The process cannot be accelerated or otherwise altered by any known chemical or physical means, but simple decontamination methods can be employed.

The basic principle is the liberal use of water. Large surfaces such as streets, walls, etc., can be dealt with by hosing down, as with fire-fighting equipment. The water used should be disposed of into drains, where the removed activity is harmless. Smaller objects should be well scrubbed, and the free use of detergents is recommended for them and for personal use. Contaminated clothes can be treated likewise, though if very heavily affected, would be best disposed of altogether. Burying is the best method of disposal, and should be done as far as practicable from human environments. *Burning merely carries the radioactivity into the atmosphere, and is definitely to be avoided*. Any surface or substance with a porous or rough surface, or which for any reason cannot be thoroughly cleaned, should likewise be disposed of.

Food and water are unaffected by direct radiation (gamma rays), but might be poisoned by "fallout." The dangers resulting from taking into the body even minute amounts of radioactive material are so great, in this connection, that no precautions can be too stringent. Where buildings are still standing, and where food is covered up, there should be little risk. In the area of total destruction, however, food might well be rendered radioactive by neutrons, and should be regarded as unsafe. Otherwise, solid foodstuffs, e.g. meat, cheese, butter, would normally be rendered usable by removing a quarter of an inch all round. More porous foods such as bread, biscuits, etc., would be best ditched. Tinned foods would be safe, but wash the outside of the tin well before opening.

Water supplies might be somewhat affected, but most of the "fallout" would sink to the bottom of a reservoir, and can be removed completely by the ordinary domestic water softener.

In any case of doubt, the final arbiter of safety is the contamination meter, issued to civil defense authorities, who should be called in at once in such an instance.

In the case of some observations on soil some 80% of the deposited radioactivity was found to remain in the upper 1" layer after a year's weathering. This suggests that dangerous substances could be taken up by plants, and thus by animals and humans over a long period of time. Plants are much less sensitive than man or animals to radiation, and thus would not suffer a lot of damage themselves.

CHAPTER SIX

Long Term View

The long term effects in survivors of the bombing in Japan, as observed by an international group of physicians in 1955, give food for thought, and will be detailed briefly here.

The most serious matter in the opinion of the writer is the persistence of vague ill health, tiredness, increased susceptibility to infections and other common disorders, and mental fear or apathy. By the word persistence a term of years is meant. Evidence has been adduced indicating that physical and mental retardation of growth occurred in children who survived the bombings. This, on the larger scale of global war, could only have the most serious consequences for the human race.

Leukemia and other blood disorders, most of them invariably fatal, are still appearing in survivors at a considerably higher rate than in unexposed populations, though the peak year was 1950. Cataracts are also relatively more common; these, incidentally, are thought to be due possibly to neutron irradiation in particular; further, their distribution has suggested that the range of neutrons may be much greater than is commonly accepted.

Many male survivors have become sterile as a result of exposure to radiation and an additional rather alarming figure is the increase in major congenital malformations among the children of those people who retained fertility. An increase by 72% on the rate common in unexposed populations was found. That is to say, there have been nearly twice as many abnormalities in the children of these survivors as one would find among an average group.

The above observations refer, of course, to people who received a single large dose. What of the effects of small repeated doses spread over many years?

Some investigations carried out recently in the U.S.A. on a number of radiologists revealed some interesting facts:

The average life span of this particular group of doctors was five years less than that of other doctors, and of the general population (60 years compared with 65 years).

The incidence of fatal leukemias was eight or nine times higher than that in nonradiologist doctors.

The average number of children born to members of the group was about half that found with other physicians (1.7 compared with 3).

Finally, there were 24% (one quarter) more congenital abnormalities among children of radiologists than among those of other doctors.

The group considered must have received, due to occupational hazard, perhaps as much as 1000 r over a whole lifetime in some cases, though in others probably very much less. This is a large amount compared with what an average individual receives. The figures nevertheless illustrate clearly the menace of chronic irradiation.

Every person during his or her life is continually bombarded with radiation in small quantities. Radioactive substances are everywhere present, though in minute amounts and cosmic rays from outer space contribute to the total "background" radiation. This normally amounts to about 1.5 r in every 10 years, 9-10 r during a whole lifetime. In addition, diagnostic X-ray procedures give a certain dose to the subject. The average total receipt from this source is very difficult to estimate, but may be, for the reproductive tissues (gonads) specifically, about 3 r in 30 years.

The effect of chronic irradiation seems to be similar to the process of ageing, to the extent that each roentgen is thought to shorten life by about a ten-thousandth. This in an average human being would only amount to a total of a few weeks due to background dosage. The general debility and increased liability to infections, already referred to, while less dramatic, present a far more serious prospect in terms of world health and working capacity.

Genetic Effects

Nuclear radiation does not produce monstrosities in babies just like that. This all too common idea is mere superstition.

The reproductive tissues of all living organisms produce naturally a certain number of "mutations"; that is, hereditary patterns in sperm or egg cells which differ to a greater or lesser extent from the normal for that species. Most of these result in infertility of the cell concerned, and they therefore never actually appear in offspring. Nearly all the remainder produce deleterious abnormalities. (Beneficial changes are rare.) All that irradiation does to the gonads in doses insufficient to kill the cells, is to increase the rate of production of mutations. A total amount of about 50 r received by an individual during his or her reproductive lifetime would double the total number of mutations produced during this period. Most of the changes, while deleterious, are also "recessive." In other words, they may not appear in one or several generations but will eventually.

However, to take a very possible example, it is suggested that a total dose of 10 r (in addition to "background") to every person in the U.S.A. might well cause the actual appearance of 50,000 cases of inherited defect, over and above the present "normal" number (2%) in children of the first generation born thereafter. Continuing this rate of dosage to succeeding generations, the figure would increase, ultimately reaching a steady half-million per generation. Such a situation would pose a considerable social problem. A universal dose (U.S.A.) of only 1 r could produce several thousand cases of definite, if not obvious, handicap in the first generation. These figures, if expanded to cover the whole population of this planet, evidence the danger to which mankind is now exposing itself.

The situation cannot obviously be assessed fully at the present time. There may be a considerable error, one way or the other, with estimated figures, but the danger must not be ignored merely on this account.

How much is man-made radioactivity actually contributing at the present time to the total receipts of radiation by humans at large? Taking external radiation only, due to "fallout," wastes from atomic plants, etc., the probable amount is less than half a roentgen in 30 years to any individual. If weapon testing were to continue at a higher rate, equal to the maximum recorded so far for any one year, perhaps double this figure might be close to the truth.

This does not sound very much, and by itself is not. But taking into account increasing use of medical X-rays, and the very uncertain factor of internal radiation, the outlook is not quite optimistic. As already mentioned, a human being living in a western country receives about 3 r to the gonads from medical X-ray procedures on the average. Some indi-

31

viduals, of course, receive much more. A routine abdominal X-ray involves a total dose of 1 r per exposure, of which a proportion reaches the gonads. More prolonged investigations may deliver doses of 10-20 r. Since every least amount of radiation received produces more mutations, there is good reason to be concerned that exposure from all sources should be kept down to the barest minimum.

Internal Radioactivity

The danger of actually taking into the body radioactive substances has been referred to. It is illustrated by the fact, observed before radioactivity was discovered, that of uranium miners at Joachimsthal in Bohemia, more than 50% died of cancer of the lung. This was later found to be due to the continuous inhalation of a radioactive gas and radioactive dust.

Most of the products of an atomic explosion decay very rapidly, so that only the longer lived ones can contaminate more remote parts of the world. No such dramatic effects as that in the miners are to be expected. The most important substance appears to be an element called radiostrontium (strontium 90).

It loses half its activity in twenty years, and being chemically similar to calcium, tends to accumulate in bone, once absorbed. Furthermore, it is very difficult to remove once fixed in bone. Its presence can be a direct cause of cancer of the bone, and blood diseases, such as leukemia, can result from its action on bone marrow. In this situation, since the radiation source is so close to the living cells, the gamma and beta ray activity becomes important. Strontium 90 produces in particular beta and gamma rays.

It has been put forward that the quantity of radiostrontium in human bones at the present time is about 1 : 10,000th of the "maximum permissible amount." This does not allow, however, for several important factors. Firstly, atomic weapon tests are continuing; secondly, subsidence of dust from the upper atmosphere continues for long after a test. The effect is therefore delayed. These two items may well reduce the apparent safety margin, in the figure given, by 10-20 times. Next, the rate of uptake in children, particularly those younger than four years, is three times greater than the average. Children are also more sensitive to radiation than adults (a characteristic of growing tissues). Furthemore, the value for "the maximum permissible amount" taken in the above estimate is actually that permitted for persons occupationally in contact with radiations. The figure for the whole population should probably be at least ten times less.

These considerations practically annul the safety margin. Other substances known as carbon 14 and iodine 131, also unfissioned plutonium, appear too in appreciable amounts. When all these are taken into account, the situation appears indeed serious. The reader is now referred again to the final paragraphs of Chapter One.

CHAPTER SEVEN

Treatment of Radiation Disease

THERE IS NO SPECIFIC MEDICAL TREATMENT KNOWN AT THIS TIME FOR THE EFFECTS OF NUCLEAR RADIATION.

This is stated to clarify the matter for the reader. Some attention to the subject is not without point, however, since general first-aid measures are of value. Atomic warfare would bring about, inevitably, severe dislocation of hospital and other medical services. At Hiroshima, for example, a large proportion of the doctors and nurses in the city were killed by the explosion. As a result it might easily be several days before a casualty received proper medical attention. The main burden of handling casualties would, therefore, fall on ordinary men and women with little medical knowledge.

The intention here is to outline the basic principles of first-aid treatment of atomic casualties.

It will be recalled that there are three major effects of the bomb—burns, mechanical injuries and radiation sickness. Any of these may be met with singly in some cases, but most commonly the casualty who is in serious need of attention will be suffering in varying degree from all three. For instance, radiation sickness, uncomplicated, would probably only occur as a result of fallout at some distance from the explosion. Simple burns would be due mainly to fires after the explosion where the person had been more or less shielded from gamma flash. Mechanical injury could occur where a building had collapsed onto a shelter which afforded adequate protection from immediate blast and flash. This is to give some idea of the conditions that could be expected in particular situations. The interested reader will be able to work out other possibilities and combinations for himself.

It is important to remember that combinations of the various types of effects produce a greater likelihood of death occurring or of grave illness than might be expected from the perhaps mild nature of each particular effect. For example, in experimental rats it was found that the burn involving 30% of the body surface together with radiation to the amount of 250 r, brought about 100% deaths. Now 30% body area burn is by itself roughly an LD50 burn. 250 r alone is nonlethal. Thus combinations of moderate injuries may be highly lethal. Experiments with rats do not, of course, apply exactly to human beings but the same principle applies and will, in fact, be reinforced by the emotional and mental shock which is presumably much greater in humans.

The purpose of all first aid is twofold; firstly to

preserve the life of the patient and maintain his general well-being as far as is possible; and secondly to prevent further injury or damage and avoid complications.

The first-aid treatment of burns and mechanical injuries is fully covered in many excellent popular books. It is not intended here to repeat this material in detail but rather to discuss the handling of cases from the point of view of the particular problems encountered in atomic warfare. The reader is recommended to study more simple books on first aid and learn the principles of emergency dressings, splinting of bone fractures, prevention of bleeding and artificial respiration.

Nuclear radiation attacks the vital processes of the body in such a way as to bring about a state resembling severe shock. The maintenance of the general condition of the patient is of paramount importance —of far greater importance than the tackling of minor localized injuries. This applies also in burn and injury cases but much more so when these are complicated by a sizeable dose of radiation. Obviously if the patient is bleeding severely or has a perforated chest wound this must be dealt with first to avoid immediate death. The state of "shock," so-called, is of two kinds: true clinical shock is a physical condition of collapse of circulation as a result of loss of blood or loss of fluid volume from the circulation; it is characterised by coldness, clamminess and rapid weak pulse; emotional shock is the second variety occurring often by itself and often in combination with the first. It will be met with, as already mentioned, on a large scale in connection with atomic incidents and requires mental rather than physical ministrations as discussed in the final part of this book.

Complete rest for the patient is vital and should be fairly easy to provide even if living conditions after an incident are somewhat primitive. This and all the procedures to be described should be continued until the patient is seen by a doctor who will be able to advise on further measures and also when activity can be gradually resumed. Sedation is of value in most cases and the simple sedatives available in most households can be employed in moderation without harm. In severe cases, particularly where there is pain, morphine may be indicated but will, however, probably be only available to a few. Aspirin is useful, but as far as possible, the soluble varieties only should be used since they are less irritating to the gut. The patient should be moved as little as possible particularly if there are fractures which would be at best fixed only with makeshift splints. The patient should be kept warm.

An adequate diet is essential to maintain the general vitality of the patient. Malnutrition in Japan in 1945 contributed not a little to the severity of the symptoms experienced by victims at Hiroshima and Nagasaki. However, a certain type of diet is required. It should be semisolid and contain little irritant "roughage" (coarse bread, tough green vegetables and the less digestible parts of meat should be avoided). Too much protein is a stimulant to the body processes so that the amount of this type of food should be not more than the basic daily requirement. A total of two to four ounces of protein foods (cheese, meat, eggs) should cover this adequately. Plenty of vitamins and minerals would be valuable and could be obtained from fruit, yeast products and vegetables in the form of juices or purées.

The subject of fluids warrants special attention. Loss of fluid above the normal may occur in several ways. The injured case may have lost an appreciable amount of blood, and it is worth noting that from half to one pint can be lost into the site of a bone fracture without any more evidence of it than moderate swelling. Radiation damage to the gut brings about vomiting and diarrhea through which many pints a day can be lost. Finally the urine output may be increased on account of disturbance of the glandular mechanism controlling the kidneys. The first-aid worker will not be able to do much more than ensure a sufficient intake of fluid by mouth which should be such as to maintain a urine output of at least a quart daily. In a case where the kidneys are disturbed of course this will not be a reliable guide and more fluid should be given.

Victims who have lost much blood from any cause may need transfusions of blood, plasma, or plasma substitutes and such cases should have the first attention of doctors or trained personnel.

The body's ability to produce the substances which afford natural protection against bacterial infection is depressed by nuclear radiation. Furthermore, the depression of the blood-forming tissues means a great reduction in the white cells of the blood which constitute the first line of defense against infection. Great care must, therefore, be taken with matters of hygiene. The surface of the body generally and, of course, wounds in particular must be kept as far as possible absolutely clean and the use of mild disinfectants would not be out of place. In a debilitated individual the nose and mouth are specially subject to bacterial attack and should, therefore, be washed out frequently. Where breakdown or destruction of normal sanitary arrangements has occured, some means should be devised for disposing of excreta in such a way that minimum contamination of persons and foodstuffs is permitted.

Of therapeutics, general and specific, little can be said. Drugs would inevitably be scarce and the average person has not the training to use them safely. To discourage vomiting a good vitamin intake could be maintained as described above and the antiseasickness drugs if available are fairly harmless and may help.

Such drugs and equipment as are available will have to be reserved primarily for intermediate type cases where recovery is possible. Those who have received a small dose of radiation will normally clear up without treatment. The recipients of lethal or near lethal doses are so likely to die that it will probably be uneconomical to expend much time or expensive treatment on them. The onus of distinguishing between types of case and allocating drugs will, of course, rest with qualified physicians; first-aid measures should be applied all round.

The prevention of radiation disease is being investigated. Certain substances (notably cysteamine for the chemically minded) have been found effective if given immediately *before* exposure, but their protective action wears off so rapidly that they do not represent a practical method. However, this does indicate that there are possibilities in this line of research.

The removal of absorbed radioactive substances is a difficult matter; various dietary procedures have been tried and together with certain chemicals may be of some value. Treatment or prevention of the long term effects remain an impossibility at present.

Nevertheless, some very recent work by L. Ron Hubbard and the Hubbard Scientology Organization, has indicated that a simple combination of vitamins in unusual doses can be of value. Alleviation of the remote effects and increased tolerance to radiation have been the apparent result, and the matter is obviously worthy of further impartial research.

In all these rather depressing aspects of radiation, the factor of expense and/or scarcity of equipment looms large. The simple, if unorthodox, ideas presented in the remainder of this book are therefore doubly welcome, and the reader is asked to consider them with open-minded attention.

Book Two

"Man's Inhumanity to Man"

by L. Ron Hubbard

Foreword

The second part of this book consists of extemporaneous extracts from L. Ron Hubbard's lectures given to the Hubbard Association of Scientologists International's Congress on "Nuclear Radiation and Health" at the Royal Empire Society Hall, London, between the 12th and 15th April, 1957.

The reason for this congress, which included delegates from South Africa, New Zealand, Australia, America, India, Brazil, Israel, Germany, France and Greece, was the alarming decline in the health of the peoples of Earth in general. The Scientologist, by means of mental drills called processes, has the goal of "making the able more able," but it has been observed that the average level of decline in health has become an important factor which had to be investigated.

L. Ron Hubbard, the founder of Scientology, observed the necessity of solving this factor as people's problems regarding their general health level detracted more attention than was necessary during processing. In other words, it became vital that the cause for this occurence be found and ameliorated.

After a period of two years in which Hubbard and a team of research Scientologists investigated brainwashing, nuclear radiation, etc., the British organization invited him to submit his findings to Scientologists in Europe, hence the congress.

Scientology, the science of knowing, came out of the same crucible as the atomic bomb. It was developed for good, not evil. For that reason Scientology has been called *that branch of atomic science which deals with human ability*. As its founder has been trained as one of the first nuclear physicists it can be seen why.

JOHANN TEMPELHOFF, D.D.

The Real Threat of Atomic Radiation

The subject of this lecture is radiation and health, its general aspect and the role that organizations such as Scientologists play in this field.

All I wish to demonstrate in this lecture is that the H-bomb and radiation create, in the main, hysteria, and that that is their greatest danger at this time.

As we speak of this you should realize that on the face of earth today there is no ready solution for radiation. We are talking about an unsolved problem, one which could be solved with some brilliant work. The Scientologist is already doing his part in solving it.

Nuclear fission is an interesting subject and deeply concerns the Scientologist. Why? Because Scientologists are interested in health and where there is radioactive atmosphere there is also a declining health rate.

Tiredness, exhaustion, hopelessness and the inability to see any future all go hand in hand. These are the Four Horsemen of today. If I tell you that one of the most important parts of human thinkingness is the ability to confront a future, or to have a future or to find a future, and if I tell you at the same time that nuclear fission says to you: "You will have no future," you can at once see that it has depressing aspects which have not been broadly presented to the world.

A man's future normally depends upon his own actions, his ability to get on with his fellow men, his ability to do work, to make himself personable, to maintain his home and raise his family. Not so long ago, in the Southwest part of the United States— which is incidentally saturated with radiation at this time—a medical doctor, an apparently sane man, after investigating the effects of radiation on health and the way it influenced the future, shot and killed his wife, five children and committed suicide leaving a note saying that there will be no future for this race.

This is fairly grim. Hardly anybody knows anything at this time about nuclear fission. Hardly anybody has any idea of what it is doing and here is probably its greatest menace. It is something which hangs in the air, something which sneaks in upon you, touching you and of which you aren't aware.

We have man living in a mysterious world. He is getting sick from types of illnesses which his medical doctors do not glibly diagnose. The doctor says it is gastroenteritis but of an unknown kind since he has not seen it before, and the patient has the idea that it may be radiation that is making him ill.

Because he does not know and because this cannot be proven easily and because some governments today have been somewhat less than straightforward on this subject, there is no easy way to know what is taking place.

In other words, a man raises his family. He has lots of children running around. They are going to go to school and he goes to work every day to get money to support his family. He wants his children to be healthy and one day they are sick. He cannot understand quite how or why, but one day he realizes that there is a high probability that his children will never grow to maturity. They are growing into a world which will not be there and he says, "What is the use then? Why should I raise this family?"

That is very depressing and fills one with grave concern. I would never join the ranks of those who attempt to drive people into hysteria simply for their own gratification or political ambitions; I would at least attempt to discover and let people know the truth—truth without hysteria or question marks.

The Greatest Danger of Radiation

Today we are going to take up the subject of this question very brutally, bluntly and factually, and at the same time stress this message: "THE GREATEST DANGER OF RADIATION IS NOT SMALL INVISIBLE PARTICLES DRIFTING THROUGH THE AIR, BUT THE HYSTERIA OCCASIONED BY

49

THE PROPAGANDA, THE MISUNDERSTANDING AND THREAT WHICH ACCOMPANIES IT."

Hysteria is the danger, not the particle, because this hysteria could, unless expertly handled, grow to such a peak that whole populaces could go entirely out of control of their own governments.

There are two ways of going out of control. The one is to get upset and throw bricks through the prime minister's window or at the White House. The other way is simply to lie down and quit from the game of life.

Somebody comes along and says, "Here, here, the streets are dirty. Clean them," and the sweeper says, "Why? What's the use? There is no future!"

Somebody says to the school teacher, "Teach these children," and she replies, "Why teach them? They will never live," and somebody says, "The factory's wheels must turn," and the mechanics say, "We are tired."

That is an aspect which the great powers may or may not have thought over. But it is the only aspect of real danger in the H-bomb at this time and it is the main aspect in which we, as Scientologists, are interested.

The Russian Bomb

Russia is probably the foremost offender in this since the Russian bomb has the characteristic of having more raw gamma than other bombs. The United

States has finally solved the problem of waste radiation in an explosion to a marked degree. U.S. bombs don't spray radiation all over the place to the degree that they did when they were first being tested. That has been a direct result of testing and they have got that problem solved. There now may be no real reason to go on testing, except perhaps to impress Russia.

On the other side Russia has not so refined her bomb and the amount of raw gamma which is being discharged is very serious. The bomb is not just exploding as a bomb, but many times as much gamma is being released as it should be. So it makes a very dangerous atmospheric condition.

In the early stages of radiation the situation with regard to testing is quite serious, but as it goes on this seriousness becomes quite minimal. In other words, there are less and less dangerous waste products.

My own Background

One might well ask what I know about this subject. It is amusing that I should know anything about it because the basic reason for working in the field of the mind, Scientology, was based upon the use to which this information was being put in the early 1930s.

I was a member of the first class in nuclear physics —we called it Atomic and Molecular Phenomena, of which nuclear physics is just a small part—which was taught at the George Washington University. It was not at that time and is not now, an open and shut subject. It permitted speculation. Atomic and molecular phenomena was simply no more or less than, "What did electrons and nuclei do when one did something to them?" and that included what happened to bread crumbs when one threw them about.

This whole subject was being grooved down, not by anybody's choice or selection, to a very forceful study of splitting the atom and the splitting of the atom at that time was a fact. Everybody thinks the atomic bomb suddenly blew into our knowledge full armed in 1943 and 1945 when we bombed Japan. This is not true. The atomic bomb technology was developed rather fully for decades before anybody put it to use. It requires somebody to sit down and write a check. The technology was there, but the tremendous amount of money necessary to develop nuclear physics was not given. It was a war which made that possible and the check was written for three billion dollars and so we actually got a bomb manufactured.

Nuclear physicists were in the '30s known as "Buck Rogers" boys—the comic strip character of science fiction—and there was nothing the nuclear physicist could be used for. He had no background that could be used in industry. Rocketry was completely flat and left to the Germans and the Russians. Any field that he might have entered had no real use for him, so he either employed himself as a civil engineer running a survey or something of the sort, or he turned to some other field of endeavor.

So after I finished training, the Depression was on in full and the only use I could put this Buck Rogers information to was science fiction. Like so many later physicists I wrote science fiction for years and that was the only remunerative use I made of this material.

But as far as nuclear physics is concerned the only use I ever made of any of the material directly and intimately was to try to define the tiniest particle or wavelength of energy in this universe.

I realized that I would probably find that small particle in the human mind. I did a calculation to see how memory is stored, and developed a theory that was called "The Protein Molecule Theory of Memory Storage". I wrote this simply as a possibility and then demonstrated later on in this thesis that it was an impossibility. The idea was that there were two to the 21st power binary digits of neurones in the brain and each one of these with a hundred holes in it would act as a storage battery for human experience. I did the calculation and found that if you took all the perceptions and observations of a three months' period and stored them, even this vast number of neurones was not sufficient to hold it. This theory came back from Austria as an Austrian development and in fact with exactly the same computation—I found that mine had a mathematical error in it which I made back in 1938—and they didn't say that it was unworkable. They said that this was the way in which human memory is stored.

The search for the smallest particle led me over to the psychology department of the George Washington University and I asked what proved to be very embarrassing questions, such as "How do people think?" which was never answered but incoherently explained in a most unscientific manner. I was in the field of engineering and here one had, for instance, a person such as a specialist in chemical material. When one went over to him to ask a question, he answered it. With a shock I received the information that there was no functioning department devoted to the human mind which could scientifically answer questions about it. Hence my interest quickened.

They could tell me a lot about the reactions of rats when put in mazes, but not how rats thought. They said the subject was called psychology, meaning 'psyche," a Greek word meaning "spirit," but in the same breath told me that they didn't believe in a soul because it couldn't be proven. Here was, for my information, a serious hole in man's culture.

They considered the mind as a brain which had actions and reactions of various kinds, but as nearly as I could understand it, it had to be a mathematical subject which should be developed by observation of people. As far as I could discover, none of these things were being done. Psychologists were not mathematicians and did not know how to develop a theory mathematically and extrapolate it in such a way as to get a prediction of what the condition was.

When I asked where this subject came from, they answered that it was born in 1879, in Leipzig, Germany, from the mind of a man called Wundt. But they had no textbook written by him and nobody seriously contributed to this subject and I got a suspicion that somebody was kidding somebody and was pretending to know something about something about which nothing was known.

I was shocked to discover that there was no Anglo-American technology of the mind—only some German guesses. This, to me, was a serious thing. We are given to believe that the field of the mind is very definitely covered, that a great deal is known about it. I had just been studying a subject, nuclear physics, which threatened to disturb the mental equilibrium of the world in future years. "Someday somebody will want to know something about the mind," I said to myself and so I went on about my work, studied and got a degree in the subject, whatever good that was, and as I wrote and lived and fought through the Second World War, my attention stayed on this research project. The materials just kept mounting up.

It seemed to me that it became more and more necessary that man should know something more about the mind. In view of the fact that some of my friends in World War II went a bit off their heads, I found that there was some use for knowledge about the mind and thinkingness.

Man Is Not a Machine

I found through continuous observation that *"basically man is not a machine, however much he loves machinery. Whatever man consists of, he is basically NOT EVIL, he is merely ignorant."*

With these findings came a considerable amount of technical information concerning man's reactions to various stimuli such as electricity, light, smell—various types of reactions which culminate now in his reaction to nuclear fission.

The Revolt of the American Nuclear Physicists

At the end of World War II a friend of mine, Lt. Commander of the Coast Guard, Johnny Arwine, and myself went to the California Institute of Technology (Cal Tech)—to meet with a great many old time atomic physicists who had been at the project that dropped the original bomb—from Alamogordo. It was our intention to organize these people so that some sort of sensible control could be monitored across the bomb. Nobody had thought about it at this date and Johnny Arwine and I were still in uniform. We were both in the world of engineering, then in the world of arts and then finally in the service. Neither of us had a thing to do with atomic fission in its development.

We got these atomic physicists together. I took the chair and Arwine addressed them. We spoke of using a propaganda weapon against anyone who would use atomic fission further against the human race. We planned to use any means we had to educate the people in the world concerning this.

The nuclear physicists were already so furious about this that Arwine and I could not control the meeting. We could keep them in their place, tell them to talk but we couldn't get across any thought that was even rationally workable. These men said one thing: "We wish to overthrow the government of the United States by force."

That is an astonishing chapter in the field of nuclear physics which only a few of us know about. There was a revolt and later on offices opened in the United States to propagandize the public in a movement led by the late Albert Einstein.

Arwine and I failed and withdrew our support from that meeting and did our best to calm them. We reported the findings to the Navy Department and the President. We said that we could not associate our names with this organization. But the atomic physicist did try and he is not going to do much more because Albert Einstein is dead.

The other day I read the list of atomic scientists who are now dead. It is practically the whole roster. They died of leukemia, cancer and the very diseases radiation sickness breeds. They died to a marked degree of radiation, mostly I suppose mentally because they had exerted a tremendous overt act against the world and had been unable to repair it in any way.

That is clear fact and not propaganda. I am just stating that there was a background where the nuclear physicist did attempt to revolt. The punishment taken against him was severe. The information given here is not even vaguely confidential and I am not in the possession of any confidential material.

From that time on it was what seemed to be a lost cause. We knew that the world was certainly in danger from the fury of atomic war, but I am afraid that none of us were clever enough to realize that continued testing would take place since it seemed so stupid. None of us counted on the factor that the airs of the earth would be polluted with radiation. That was not part of our understanding. So the only new thing that has happened here, has been that a certain carelessness for public welfare has caused continued testing of the atomic bomb. This may bring about sufficient hysteria and upset on the part of the general public that government itself will become impossible. This is the extreme possibility.

I do not believe that atomic fission will continue being tested to a point where everybody dies. But I do believe that bombs will continue being tested to a point where everybody could be worried to a point where a great deal of the ability would be gone out of society.

I am not talking against the United States. The United States was simply the first to develop this. Since that time the bomb has gotten into much more irresponsible hands in getting into Russian hands.

In the final analysis man has done an unfortunate thing and unless defenses can be found and the public educated he may very well pay a dreadful price.

What Is Radiation?

Radiation is either a particle or wavelength, nobody can say for sure. One moment everybody says it is a wavelength and the next they say it is a particle. Let's define it as *a capability of influencing matter, and that that capability can be exerted across space.*

A bullet can influence matter and the only different definition we would make in atomic radiation is that it does it more so. Shoot a man and he dies. Spray a man with radiation and he dies more slowly, but he dies.

A man does very specific things in the process of dying from atomic radiation. He dies in a certain way.

The oddity is that if you throw a handful of bullets at somebody he doesn't get particularly upset as the bullets are just being tossed at him. Supposing tomorrow you throw another handful at him and repeat this for some days; he would simply say that somebody every day throws bullets at him. All those bullets never did add up to being shot with one bullet. That is the single difference with atomic radiation. Today we throw a few rays at somebody and tomorrow we again throw a few rays at the same man and continue for a while doing this, and all of a sudden he dies—as though he has been shot with a bullet. In other words, radiation is cumulative.

If one wants to know exactly what it does and how it does it, one would go to listen to any nuclear physicist giving a technical lecture on the subject. There are all sorts of interesting data about it such as that if one took uranium and refined it one would get an intolerant element known as plutonium. If too much plutonium gets smashed together with too much plutonium it explodes, gamma rays spray about, other elements are influenced and so forth. Plutonium is an intolerant element. It is artificially manufactured and very intolerant of itself.

The way one makes an atomic bomb is quite interesting. One takes a piece of plutonium at, let's say, the end of a stick and another piece at the other end of the stick. One fixes it so that the back piece of plutonium will slide and hit the front piece of plutonium and then simply throws the stick. When the front piece of plutonium hits the ground, the back piece hits the front piece and it explodes. And that is a bomb! When it explodes it releases a tremendous amount of gamma, and many other items much too lengthy to catalogue. These items, each one in some separate way, might have a deadliness of their own. The various materials that are used as containers of these bombs, such as cobalt 60, have the capability of killing people practically at a breath. So it has been made a bit more deadly than it already is. All an atomic bomb is, is the method of getting plutonium to intolerate itself and explode.

What is important is that such bombs when they explode leave in the atmosphere a residue of gamma, strontium 90 and several other elements which cause a widespread coverage of the countryside with a deadly substance. It floats in the air and unites with the dust particles which then settle on the ground or still drift along causing an air pollution unlike T.N.T.

If somebody tells one not to worry about the atom bomb since it is just a bigger kind of T.N.T. bomb, this person is being very nonfactual because atomic fission and T.N.T. are not comparable. It is the blast, the burn, the fragments of T.N.T. that does the injury. It is the radiation plus the blast, the burn, heat, particles and explosion that does the injury in the atomic bomb.

The atomic bomb is like T.N.T. united with poison gas which does not settle or dissipate. It is an entirely different thing to be bombed with T.N.T. and poison gas than it is to be bombed with a T.N.T. bomb.

Air Pollution

When we speak of this residue of the exploded bomb, we speak about radiation in the air or air pollution. This residue stays in the air for a very long time before it comes down to earth and the way they blow these bombs nowadays is to explode them so high that the residue will not drift down to the surface for another ten years.

Political Factors

Whatever political purpose there may be in exploding a bomb, it is quite certain that the continuous testing of bombs is destructive. In some people's eyes it may have enough political connotation that they think it is necessary to go on testing bombs. These bombs must be released to keep people aware of the fact that they are in the possession of certain governments. Russia is trying to keep in the picture to show the people of earth that she has atomic bombs. In other words, we have an arms race which is out in plain view and which is different from building a battleship and sending it around the world.

We explode a bomb to show we have one. Nobody is to be condemned for this providing he does not understand at the time that he is widely endangering health.

It seems as though the Russian and American governments are actually of the opinion that not enough nuclear fission explosions have been done to date to damage the health of mankind. However, none of the releases which have been put out so far are convincing on this subject and the public is not convinced. As a result we fall into two schools of thought—the government release and the public reaction.

The Public Reaction to Atomic Radiation

The public reaction is best expressed by men of the press and these have a tendency to fight back against the government releases. Governments say that although they don't know what the roentgen (r) count must be in order to be fatal, they nevertheless feel, by experiments which they have not made, that the amount of radiation in the atmosphere at this time will not kill, deform or derange more than 6,000 babies in the coming year.

The press gets hold of this and quite righteously criticizes this statement. It asks: "Where is your data and what is it? How do you know? What do you mean about supposing that 6,000 babies are not important? Suppose one of them was yours?"

The Question Mark

Out of this we get a tremendous question mark.

WHETHER RADIATION IS FLOATING ACROSS THE WORLD OR NOT IS NOT THE POINT. THERE IS A QUESTION MARK FLOATING ACROSS THE WORLD. Is it or isn't it there? The question mark is radiation itself.

How Radiation Hurts a Human Body

How does radiation hurt a human body? Nobody

can tell, but the following may be crudely stated. A sixteen foot wall cannot stop a gamma ray but a body can. We thus get down to our number one medical question: How is it that gamma rays go through walls but don't go through bodies? We can plainly see that a body is less dense than a wall.

We have to go into the field of the mind if we cannot find out the answer in the field of anatomy.

Resistance

I can fortunately tell you what is happening when a body gets hurt by atomic radiation. It RESISTS the rays! The wall doesn't resist the rays and the body does.

A gamma ray doesn't often settle in the body. It goes through but its passage through the body creates a sensation of some kind, which, if too recurrent, is resisted on the part of the cells and the body. This resistance itself brings about the "stop" chaos that one observes in "no future."

The reaction of the mind to the bomb is that we have "no future" any more. The body says, "Stop the gamma. Stop, stop . . ." and as this is going on all the time when we are bombarded with radiation, the body finally says, "I am stopped." The body senses that there is an influence around it which it must stop because its survival is being endangered. It feels that it must *resist* the rays in one way or another and the body gets hurt.

Oddly enough cosmic rays and X-rays act the same way.

The Slight Effects of Radiation

The slighter effects of radiation, very generally and rapidly, take on some of these aspects: hives, skin irritation, flushes of one kind or another, gastro-enteritis, sinusitis and "colds," colitis, exhausted achy feelings in the bones, glandular malfunction, and so forth. We are here looking at effects one would normally experience from an overdose of radiation.

The Serious Effects of Radiation

The serious reactions of atomic radiation all sum up to cancer—bone cancer, lung cancer, skin cancer and so on. If a medical doctor inspected this very closely he would find that leukemia had an association with cancer.

Cancer merely says, "We cannot go on. Procreation from here on is impossible on a cellular level." The cells feel that they can no longer procreate and instead of procreating in co-operation with the body the cells simply procreate in a wild and abandoned manner in some other direction. In other words, the cells are driven into an independent action or reaction in the lines of growth.

That is one type of cancer. The other basic type is simply erosive, corrosive, death of tissue, malignancy. Both are associated with "no future" as a mental reaction.

What Man Faces

That is what man faces, not much, merely obliteration. There are other less important, less dramatic things which lie between the two effects of radiation.

For instance, a man who was never tired, might one day start feeling tired. We find that he might be holding a mental image picture of Trafalgar Square. We ask him what happened at Trafalgar Square and he cannot think of anything. He wasn't run over by a taxi, nothing startled him. Nothing happened there to account for this picture being held in his mind and yet he is "stuck mentally" in Trafalgar Square. Why? He got a blast of radiation at that point. The wind blew around the corner and stuck him in that spot because the wind had radiation in it. His body sensed it. He resisted it. He "stuck his sense of time" in Trafalgar Square.

Whenever one gets one of these overwhelming mysteries one gets mentally upset. How would such a man react? He would one day get tired of being tired. He would feel that he is going to die anyway and so he might as well do something desperate. He is being told to do something. He feels that he should react and he doesn't know which direction to react to. That is the main problem. He cannot account for this effect upon himself, so he thinks that there *must* be some accounting for it. So he assigns a cause to some other agency than radiation.

The Misassignment of Causes for Sickness

One will sooner or later find this man saying, "What is making us ill here in London is *cats*!" He thinks that if he kills all the cats everybody will be in good condition again. There is no accounting for where this sudden enthusiasm came from killing all the cats in London. But somebody got the idea and said "The reason we don't feel well is the cats. They're carrying some disease or other so we'll just kill all cats."

Somebody else will say, "It's the government. Therefore we should kill off the government." This would be misassignment of cause. Someone might say, "Well actually it's probably lorry gas." Then one would have people lying down on the street preventing any buses from moving in London. These people will be looking for a cause for their ill health, and if they cannot find one, they will assign it rather ridiculously.

Every time one gets some kind of national question mark of this character, misassignment of cause takes place and people start doing strange things. Great Britain might not be in the war at all but her populace would possibly feel they were fighting.

For example, a man was on a tug in Pearl Harbor when Japanese were flying over and bombing the harbor. He told his men to pick up potatoes and throw them at the planes. The sailors stood there throwing potatoes at planes three or four hundred feet above them.

These men knew what was wrong. They knew it was the bombers and the bombs. If they couldn't do anything at all, they would have turned around and said that it was the captain's fault. Having no outlet for their expression of outrage and not being able to define the cause, they would fictitiously assign it to something else.

Because men cannot do anything to strike back against this thing called radiation they are then liable to strike at things which are not connected with it. One might thus eventually have a tumultuous, hard to control society. *That is the only real danger in my mind of radiation at large at this time*, for the United Nations may very well produce some sort of solution to put a brake on the testing of atomic bombs.

The Primary Problem

The primary problem we face today is not the control of governments who are failing to control testing and radiation but actually the problem of continuing to control a populace which may get too tired to go on living, or may revolt into a hysteria which defies control.

One can see the beginnings of that right now in the newspapers. People are becoming upset about radiation. We may say that if we influence the governments to stop this testing and issue sensible information on the subject of radiation, inform the people what it is really all about, that would be a sensible course. But I don't know if we can, at this time or place, take such a course.

We have, though, a secondary course which is quite well open and that is appertaining to the control of civil populaces' problems. How does one keep people fairly calm, cool and collected, braced up to it in the face of this much danger and trouble? Because if one can keep them in such a mental state by showing them that they aren't going to be killed, by giving them some hope of one kind or another, they will come through where they otherwise would not.

I state again that *the danger in the world today in my opinion, is not the atomic radiation which may or may not be floating through the atmosphere, but the hysteria occasioned by that question.*

LECTURE TWO

Radiation in War

This lecture is about radiation in war. I have here a newspaper article brought to me a few minutes ago by a Scientologist which mentions that Harold Stassen has just gone to the United Nations to suggest that all future fissionable materials should be exclusively used for peaceful purposes.

There is a great deal of pressure on the governments of the world to stop bomb tests and not to pollute the atmosphere. But such pressure is not what causes this type of statement which has appeared in newspapers from time to time.

For instance, Russia makes a statement that we should be very peaceful about this, and the United States makes a similar statement and the other nations all urge the cessation of atomic bomb testing. In this lecture I think I can show why people are willing to listen to such statements as this. The news that follows is more important than Mr. Stassen's statement.

I am sure that President Eisenhower would abolish testing if at any time he could feel with conscience that he is protecting the United States. However, he feels that he must protect his country and that the atomic bomb is a weapon which is capable of doing that. Governments like the United States, Britain and Russia are pressured consistently much closer to home than some church organizations or public group.

The German Nuclear Physicists Revolt

In my earlier lecture I told you about the American nuclear physicists' revolt which failed in the United States in 1945. Now just below this news item about Mr. Stassen's statement is a very interesting news item which doesn't have the space and headlines it deserves. It reads: "Scientists won't make H-bombs. Eighteen top German scientists led by 78-year-old Otto Hahn, a pioneer of nuclear fission, today told Chancellor Adenauer, 'We refuse to take any part whatsoever in making, testing or firing atomic weapons.' "

The revolt which failed in the United States is continuing in other countries. It is very difficult to find a nuclear physicist today who will stand in and read the meters, who will do the mathematical computations or anything else. These men are men too. They have families and they know very well that their own children, their wives and themselves could be made extremely ill and that civilization, which they have been brought up to cherish, is likely to disappear in the next war. This is as undesirable to them as it is to us or any other citizen anywhere else in the world.

71

What is a government up against? Why doesn't a government simply say, "Well, this is an undesirable weapon, and we will at once dispense with it"?

The Use of Science in War

Modern governments have gone very deeply into the world of science in order to execute their battles. At one time governments depended exclusively upon a man with a weapon in his hand. They depended on him to go in and bring a better state of compliance on the part of some neighbor. They no longer depend on that soldier. They have developed weapons that are much more important to them than the courage of infantry. These weapons have also already been used in World War II, so we are not talking about fictitious weapons. Every bit of scientific lore which can be accumulated by scientists in the hope that it may better the lot of their fellow men, has eventually been employed in the destruction of men.

This is a rather hideous commentary on the practices of man and begins long before we ordinarily think of its having begun. In 1870 Hotchkiss desired to end war by developing a weapon so violent that no one would dare fight war and he invented the Hotchkiss gun. It has been used in every war since.

One hears of the Nobel Peace Prizes. Nobel discovered dynamite. T.N.T. and dynamite were invented to make war so horrible that man would not fight it. We see a reflection of that aim in the Nobel

Peace Prizes. Nevertheless this man invented something that laid European cities and London in ruins in World War II. He wanted no more war, so through threat and fear and duress he thought to drive men into an opinion that war could no longer be fought.

This has always been the case. One hired a big enough army, armed it well, taught the enemy that it was sufficiently ferocious and thought that war would be too horrible for an enemy to fight. But every time it has brought war. Evidently war is not a good method of controlling other nations since it has never worked. Man should observe from the errors of the past that this method never will work.

Scientific Weapons

Today man is using scientific weapons. The scientific complexities which lie back of aeroplanes, T.N.T. bombs and so forth are quite fantastic. Some of them, such as the proximity bombs have 2,000 separate connections per weapon. The most intricate thing one ever saw is one of these radar shell anti-aircraft weapons. And they are quite deadly. They throw ammunition up into the vicinity of an aircraft and as it explodes it is made certain by the aircraft radar that the plane is in its centre. These are called proximity shells. It was those shells which made it possible for U.S. battleships to sail close to the very shores of Japan during the end days of World War II.

Brainwashing—a Political Weapon

How much further has man gone?

In 1927 or 1928 he developed a political weapon called "brainwashing." A Russian by the name of Pavlov, who had been experimenting with the reactions and conditioning of dogs, was brought to the Kremlin by Stalin. He was put in a separate room and was asked to write everything he knew concerning the conditioning and actions of animals as it might apply to the human being. He wrote a 400-page manuscript which since that day has never left the Kremlin.

Immediately after that in 1928 we saw the astonishing factor of cabinet ministers and Russian officials confessing to the most outrageous crimes. These men walked up before the bar of justice and at their own trials condemned themselves glibly. That was the first the world saw of brainwashing. In the Korean war less expert people used these same techniques on the troops who were employed by the United Nations in the Korean war.

Brainwashing is child's play. One shouldn't be very worried about brainwashing. Some twenty per cent of the soldiers who are captured in battle will crack up in prison camps and brainwashing does not violate this percentage. The man who invented it and the people who have used it are not sufficiently acquainted with the mind in order to make it very effective. An inspection of brainwash-

ing cases demonstrates that it worked only occasionally.

What Brainwashing Is

Brainwashing is a very simple mechanism. One gets
a person to agree that something *might be* a certain
way and then drives him by introverting him and
through self-criticism to the possibility that it is
that way. Only then does a man believe that the
erroneous fact is a truth. By a gradient scale of
hammering, pounding and torture, brainwashers are
able to make people believe that these people saw and
did things which they never did do. But its effectiveness is minor as Russia does not know enough about
the human mind.

Nevertheless, Pavlov himself directing the use of his
original manuscript was certainly effective on the top
Russian officials in those treason trials that shocked
the world in 1928. These men never did anything that
they admitted to having done. They simply had been
conditioned into believing they had.

Brainwashing was attempted on Mindszenty. It
didn't work, but for a moment he· quivered and
wavered at his trial. Brainwashing is not an effective
weapon, but it could be worked on, developed and
with the information about the mind denied to the
rest of the human race and kept secret, brainwashing
could be made to be effective.

If that happened society could be made into slaves.

Knowledge about the Mind Must Not Be Kept Secret

Anything which is known about the mind and has benefited human beings, must be permitted to exist in public view. It must be possible for anyone to lay his hands on how to undo such things as brainwashing. Therefore there must never be a restriction of technologies concerning the human mind. These must never be buried. There must never be a hierarchy in some universities that dictates the only technique that may be used or invalidates the abilities of people who can work in the field of the mind.

It would be a very dangerous thing to the human race if such a group existed. Why? Because we have this thing called brainwashing and because it became a war weapon.

How to Undo Brainwashing

How does one undo brainwashing? One simply brings the person up to present time. He is stuck in time— the time he was "brainwashed." He is thrust into the past. He is completely introverted and all one has to do is to extrovert him, let him see where he is, how he is and what he is doing and brainwashing desensitizes. It is not even a problem to the Scientologist. We have undone many cases who have been brainwashed with success, but it is a problem to the governments of the world.

Governments fear that if we go into the next war

and the enemy captures many of our troops, throws them into prison camps and brainwashes them, they will then so derange and disarrange and change these soldiers' loyalties that these men will return to their own country as saboteurs and provocateurs. It worries governments as this is a dreadful thing, for they depend on loyalty and the fact that it might be possible to change the loyalties of individuals worries governments.

Any Scientologist with an E-Meter could tell if somebody's loyalty has been changed. That is not even a problem, but it is a problem of the governments and they are working in their own way trying to solve that problem. However, they don't seem to be making much progress.

The government itself is threatened by the weapon called brainwashing. Here is the head of state. He appoints some secret police and they play false and grab hold of the head of state and brainwash him. How can one ensure his cabinet ministers that as he sits there at the head of the table he is not dictating the policy of some foreign nation? Such a condition could exist. It could happen.

Here is a weapon which is no good. It has not proven very useful. It is simply dangerous and it worries people. But it is a modern scientific weapon and its future history can only be dismal because the only thing it can do is to shake the foundations of the governments which employ it. Russia must have various organizations posting guards every night around its leaders to make sure that nobody slips in and brainwashes them. How can one guarantee their loyalty to Russia?

If one suspects that one of one's associates has been brainwashed, the best thing to do is to get hold of a Scientologist for he can handle the matter with ease. But the real trouble is that few people have the skill to detect the fact and then fewer still have the ability or technology to undo it. Because of this it becomes a terrible weapon.

It takes a very unsettled, unstable neurotic personality to succumb to brainwashing. He has to be mad already because Pavlov never did find out how to drive a really sane man insane. He merely found out how to utilize incipient madness.

The Problems of the Governments

I only talk to you about brainwashing to show that governments do have problems. One says that radiation is not this kind of problem? A government uses radiation against the populations of other countries or against its own, therefore radiation could not be this kind of problem?

It is. Radiation is much more a deadly threat to a centralized government than it ever was to a population. That is an adventurous statement to make, but Russia will rue the day that she dabbled in atomic fission as a war weapon. How is this?

The History of War

One has to understand something about the history of war. Big tomes have been written on this subject, but I will briefly mention something about it.

The history of war is the history of CONTROL. The end goal of war is to throw out of its control the population of another government. This is just a little more advanced than the last definition of war in about 1792, which was rather lengthier and is summed up as follows: "to compel some compliance and obediance on the part of the other government." That is not really what war is supposed to do. War is supposed to throw another nation's population out of control so that one can supplant the government or its attitudes and give them their population back in control again.

War against the Population

Modern warfare is levied against the populations of other governments, on the theory that they will fall away from the controlling government and the controlling government will collapse and can then be changed.

Alexander the Great did this much more rapidly. Whenever he went up against an enemy ruler he took his Companion Cavalry, rode through the ranks, found the enemy ruler and cut him to pieces. This was his idea of tactics and strategy. He has been criticized as a strategist because he didn't meddle with populations. He simply went and annihilated the other government. He wasn't really against the government or the household of the ruler. He just killed the head of state and in the case of Darius even married his wife. He didn't worry much about the population. He merely took it over.

He was very direct. He took the person out of control of the government by killing him. Modern war philosophy is different. One hammers and pounds the population one way or another until it can no longer be controlled. They figure that the government then collapses. This is the basis on which modern war is fought.

Antipopulation Weapons

So now we use weapons which are antipopulation weapons. They didn't use a short sword at the throat of Kaiser Bill. They used machine guns aimed at the troops of Kaiser Bill. They overran the towns and villages and population. More modernly they bomb the factories and cities of Kaiser Bill so as to make the population give up. The population can no longer continue, therefore the government can no longer continue. In other words, the population is out of control.

The Ideal Weapon

What would be an ideal weapon to bring about this

state? I am afraid it is a very sinful answer, namely, tested radiation. If one kept testing radiation other populaces would get nervous. They would say, "Can't we have peace one way or another?" In the face of radiation-impregnated atmosphere one has a different attitude here and a government which does not have radiation is apt to get worried about the governments who do, because an effect is being rendered against their population which they themselves cannot halt. There is no defense against radiation, remember that.

So one actually has the end goal of war being executed in times of peace simply by sabre rattling. But this again is a very old philosophy. One took a large armed force and paraded it and everybody said: "We don't want anything to do with that army. Let's have peace with those people." We couldn't get any enthusiasm of the populace towards fighting. However, this is more sweeping since it is not localized against the other government and so we have encountered an unlimited weapon without direction since atomic testing is as deadly against one's own population as it is against the population of another nation.

Here we get political problem number one of the atomic bomb. It can throw the very government that uses it out of control. It throws everybody out of control.

Unlimited Weapons

It is an historical fact that the history of weapons

has brought up several which were unlimited and against which there was no known defense at that particular period. A weapon against which there is no defense becomes an unlimited weapon and when these have appeared on the stage of man, governments have collapsed. Formal government cannot exist in the presence of an unlimited weapon.

This is a very factual, down-to-earth statement and it is something which appears in the textbooks of strategy and tactics. When one has a weapon against which there is no defense, governments become extinct.

The First Unlimited Weapon

There is a period which is covered mostly by legend between 1500 and 1200 B.C. where an unlimited weapon swept out of the steppes of Russia and smashed any civilization which existed in Europe. It destroyed it so thoroughly that we haven't any records of it having happened, except in the poems of Homer. Such early periods were considered very legendary until a German found the ruins of the city of Troy—and it was concluded that Homer was writing about a real fight. However, according to Homer, this occurred before the history of Troy.

The horse and sword was the unlimited weapon which swept out from the steppes of Russia across Europe just as it did in 1200 A.D. The nations of Europe were without defense against cavalrymen.

Infantry could not stand to a cavalryman. He was mounted, swift, his sabre and sword penetrated any existing armor and with or without formation or plan he could overrun any city. Nothing known then could stop him. It was not until recent times that men put a pike in alternate files and so stopped cavalry from charging and wiping up the infantry—Napoleonic times, which is very recent. But nothing like this stood against the cavalrymen as they came in from Russia.

These men carried everything before them. There was nothing like an organized government throughout the length and breadth of the Mediterranean or Europe for 200 years.

Then somebody got a defense for it and once more governments could exist because a defense existed against the man mounted on a horse with his sword. That invention was the wall. That seems like an elementary invention but it certainly stopped this inrush of cavalry, and men could build a wall around their cities, could enclose their populaces and protect them against these expeditions which had rendered everything chaotic throughout Europe.

Not even its own government on the steppes that originally sent those men survived their use. That government too has been swallowed up and no record of its existence is left.

Where there is an unlimited weapon there is no government possible. Why? Because no city can be possible. Nobody can sit down anywhere and govern from anywhere. The moment one actually sat down and started governing and communication lines started coming in and taxes were being collected, some irresponsible guerilla band, no longer part of the enemy's regular army, would sweep down and destroy the city. No police were possible. There was no policing of the roads, not even a man on a horse with a sword could fight a man on a horse with a sword. These tactics were not developed for centuries afterwards.

The only point which I am making is this: there is an unlimited weapon and it kills a government. There is a weapon against which there is no defense and it makes government impossible. That is why people are worried about the atom bomb and why they would like to get together and sign a treaty which says: "No more atomic bombs, please."

What Is a Sovereign State?

What is the definition of a sovereign state? In international law we find that a *sovereign state is an area which is under control by a government and that that government is sovereign so long as it can*—and this is the bulk of its definition— *protect the country and its people from aggressors*. When a government can no longer do so it senses the loss of some of its sovereignty.

Chiang Kai-shek would like to say that he is the

government of China, but he cannot protect any part of the land or the population of China from the communist aggression into that country. Therefore he is not the sovereign state of China. Clinging to this myth could be foolish.

A government is the government so long as it protects the land and citizens against an aggressor.

Now what does an atom bomb do to that? There is no defense against it. These weapons are going to come in as guided missiles, thousands of miles an hour. Not even a warning system can spot them before they come in. Only a few per cent would have to get through to render everything in chaos, but more importantly, there is this thing called bomb testing and saturation of the atmosphere by radiation. That itself is unstabilizing the population as it shows them it is impossible for a government to protect the population.

In the presence of an unlimited weapon a government tends to decentralize and disperse. It tends to leave the area of government and to govern from all over the place. That dispersal is already in effect in almost every nation on earth. They are no longer governing from one place, but are spreading out into other cities. We are told it is because of the housing problem or the rooms, but has one ever seen a government that wouldn't simply kick out a few tenants and make more room next door?

We look into this very carefully and find that

governments have always been upset about unlimited weapons. They don't know what to do about them and therefore they are a much bigger problem to the government than to a populace, because government itself is trying to survive as itself as a sovereign power.

If a government doesn't do something early in the career of an unlimited weapon, it no longer has the power to do anything about this. Sooner or later it has to realize that it is out of control. It will have to get into agreement with some other governments and do something about it. Their effort is continually to get some sort of treaty or agreement by which this thing won't be used.

It will have to be a very good treaty or agreement because man so far has always used, has never failed to use, the weapons he possessed.

The Value of Weapons

As far as any weapon is concerned its total value is to upset the control of a government and people by a government. All a weapon is for is to unsettle this other government and throw it out of control.

But what about a weapon that throws one's own government out of control as well? Then it ceases to be a weapon. That becomes international suicide. Governments do not articulate this but they sense it and they endeavor to act in the direction of trying to do something before it is too late. Therefore there is no real need of pressuring the government.

We Must Help the Government

People shouldn't go around pressuring the government and saying to the government that it has to abandon this or that, or mustn't do this or that There is no sense really in throwing a vast number of rotten tomatoes at somebody on a governmental level simply because he hasn't come up with a solution. The poor man probably has been sitting up all night thinking about how the government has to be kept going with such a crisis hanging over his head.

What the government needs is solutions, assistance and help. But what reaction do we get against the government? We get, "We won't work in this field any more." "We are not going to help you." Pure hysteria.

But there are people who will help governments. But the governments are so used to nobody helping them that after a while they tend to despair. It would be up to anybody who knew something about the subject to give them a hand because their power is already crumbling on the subject of atomic radiation. They need to be bolstered up in this year of 1957.

Governments of the Western world know or sense these problems. They would give anything for some good solutions.

All the government needs to know how to do is defend against an atomic bomb or get a good enough reason to abandon atomic bombs.

The Atomic Bomb Is Not a Weapon

Let's be less vague about this. One cannot success-
fully use radiation in war. To call it a war weapon or
to call it a weapon at all is being foolish. It is not a
weapon because *a weapon is something that is supposed to upset the enemy in war. Something which
kills off everybody cannot be classified as a war
weapon.* It is not useful in war.

If the United States were to bomb Russia, the
amount of radiation thrown into the atmosphere
would be so great that the population of the United
States would probably be wiped out by the effect of
its own bombs without Russia having retaliated.
There would be a tremendous amount of atomic
fission generated in the atmosphere of Russia. There
would be enough radiation in the air to seriously
affect the population of the United States.

Similarly, if Russia bombed the United States there
would be enough radiation in the atmosphere—atomic
testing for 20 years wouldn't accumulate the amount
of radiation set off—that the residue would come
back over to Russia which is but a very short distance
away over the North Pole. The next thing would be
that the Russian population would be in very poor
condition.

International Suicide

So what is this thing? As it is not a practical war

weapon one must then consider it a sort of bogyman. Everybody's hoping that nobody will find this out about it. But it might be used in war. Nations *do* commit suicide. Japan committed suicide in World War II although one may not have noticed it. She knew very well that she might not win against the United States and England combined. Japan's own officers were known to make this remark. But they had to "save face" and rather than have their honor go completely overboard they were perfectly willing to commit suicide by attacking the United States. That they were committing suicide is rather evident because they did not follow up their attacks seriously. Maybe if they hadn't been committing suicide they might have accomplished more than they did.

Russia, at its national mental level, has been known to do suicidal things and to say that the fact that it kills everybody will prevent somebody from using the bomb, is folly.

If it is a weapon, against whom is it one? Nobody knows. It really is a calamity. "It is too bad they ever thought it up," a line which I caught from a New York taxi driver. He said: "It's too bad they ever thought that thing up." That was his total comment on it.

Comment from a London taxi driver not more than 2½ hours ago: "Isn't it a shame they thought it up?" Neither man has met the other, but they are both certainly in agreement that it is not a weapon but a regrettableness.

The use of the bomb could be international suicide.

All the governments of the world are practically fixated on the idea of atomic fission, which is no weapon and puts them, as we say in Scientology, in a no-game condition. Almost any upstart little nation could suddenly come forward and develop something which *was* a weapon against which we had no immediate defense but against which there was a defense and immediately enforce its will upon the world. Another better weapon than the H-bomb could enter the world and win!

Has there ever been a simple weapon, managed by a few, that conquered large areas of Earth? There was.

The Assassins

The government of Arabia in 1200 A.D. knew very well what a weapon was. It was a trooper. With his sword and shield and bow, his formations and officers, this man drawn up in ranks was a weapon. The cavalry had worked up to a tremendous peak which one hears about in the incursions of Genghis Khan. All the governments in the Middle East knew the value of this weapon.

But there was a man by the name of Hassan (ibn) Sabbah and he had an offshoot Moslem cult of Ismalian Shiites known as the Assassins. This man and some of his people went and built a mountain stronghold which was so strong that Tamerlane himself felt dared and destroyed it much later, but only Tamerlane with all his troops could do this and then after the weapon had been in successful use for hundreds of years.

Hassan built his impregnable stronghold and in the middle of its courtyards, sitting on the peak, he built a heaven of milk and honey—with actual rivers of milk. He hired a number of houris—lovely girls—and taught them how to amuse a man. He then sent some of his men with some hashish—which was the weapon—to spot a good looking rather stupid young man. They gave him some hashish at the local inn, knocked him out and put him in a basket on a donkey and took him back to the stronghold. When he regained consciousness he was sitting in Paradise, with forty black-eyed houris and rivers of milk and honey.

And he said, as anyone would, "Where am I?" and he was told quite glibly and promptly: "Son, this is heaven. You've arrived." They let him stay around for two or three days. He found this very pleasant and wanted to stay for a long time, but they said: "You have been brought to heaven prematurely. It is necessary that you perform a small task for Allah, and if you are sure to get yourself killed in the performance of this task, and if it is successful, we can guarantee that you will appear again in heaven."

They slipped him some more hashish and took him down the mountain. He was placed in the vicinity of a palace. Now he had been told that the one deed that would get him back into heaven would be the assassination of that sultan. The sultan out for his morning ride surrounded by guards, who were the weapon of the day, would behold a young man, scimitar in hand, leaping out of the crowd and off would go the sultan's head. Of course, the guards would punch this young man full of holes and he would be dead.

Then the Old Man of the Mountain would inform the people that the Assassins were the authors of the deed and all that group had to do or infer was that some ruler at whatever distant realm or clime had done something displeasing to the Assassins and that they now required three camel loads of gold, five replacement houris and amnesty in all directions for anybody connected with their cult, and the sultans of the entire Middle East and Persia would at once despatch anything required. The sultans were terrified of these heaven-deluded youths who carried out the orders of the cult.

There was no defense against a young man who believed that by assassinating the head of another government he would regain a paradise he had already tasted. That was an unlimited weapon and it all but destroyed the governments of the Middle East. That cult lived for almost three hundred years, the most stable government, if one can call it a government, of the Middle East.

That is a mad story but history is a concatenation of madnesses. What if some government with all the other governments of the world fixated on the idea of atomic fission, say, to be extremistic, developed sleep rain? This rain would fall over a city and everybody would go to sleep. It would not hurt anybody, but people certainly would go to sleep. This is certainly not outside the scope of bacteriological weapons.

Scientists left to their own devices sit around and "dream up" weapons. The weapon I have just spoken about I heard of in a conference of scientists of Western Electric. They had it all worked out—the number of parts and materials to be used, and they were challenging a chemist from a nearby chemical works for the details. One would have thought that they were the grand council for something or another, charged with the entire responsibility for annihilating the human race. They decided that it was feasible—how one would go about constructing sleep rain—and then lost interest. They all got drunk instead of making the world go to sleep.

An Interim Weapon

Sleep rain might be called an *interim weapon*. It would be very effective because no country can govern its population if they are all asleep. They would simply wake up and find the occupying force sitting in the palace or parliament.

One of the more amazing frames of mind occurs in man when he suddenly finds his citadel invested as he wakes up in the morning. During the war some Marines had a similar idea. A group of Japanese suddenly woke up to find that they were all tied up. They couldn't move or go any place. They were totally invested. The calmness of the investing force was rather fantastic. They had slipped up on a beach unexpectedly and surrounded the barracks. There wasn't any sentry because that area was so far out of the war zone that they didn't expect any danger from anybody. The Japanese were very friendly, and even cooked rice for everybody. It may not look much like a war to us, but they certainly were under control of the investing force.

In other words, the control of the population of a base had changed, which is the end and goal of war.

There are weapons that can be developed and probably the greatest danger unknown to the government is that somebody might develop one. If everybody is spending 99% of their national income on atomic fission and somebody is willing to spend a couple of million on some mad weapon like sleep rain, we would be totally caught—and unexpectedly so.

I think it would be awfully hard for people if one dropped crows feet over a city like Cairo—crows feet

94

are little pins that have four points and when they are dropped, they land on three spikes and leave the fourth one in the air. If all one wants to do is throw a population out of control and fight some political activity that has to do with governments, why drag the rest of humanity in? Why should anybody get seriously hurt?

For instance, a certain way to destroy the United States government would be simply to introduce to the country a paper worm that would eat up all the paper. It would be impossible to fight a war.

The facts of the case then, as far as war weapons are concerned, is that they needn't be serious at all. I have read through Nikola Tesla's—the man who invented alternating currents, the Tesla coils, who spoke about ground waves, etc.—private papers and diaries which have never been exhibited to the public and he has some interesting ideas about this.

He stated that there was a feasibility of creating a standing electrical wave on one side of earth that would then appear on the other side of earth because of the spherical effect of current flows. In other words, if one were to send a freighter down into the South Pacific and have it pump electricity in the ocean—create a standing wave there—all radio communication in Moscow would become static and anything you would want to put on the air would then appear as the only message in Moscow radio stations.

Scientists dream up these weapons but normally

thinking in terms of prank. But what if a group of German or English or Argentinian scientists were liable to create one of these weapons while the rest were entirely fascinated on the subject of atomic fission? We would perhaps wake up one morning and find ourselves part of the Argentinian Empire.

The Second Danger of the Atomic Bomb

So we get the second greatest danger of the atomic bomb. It paralyzes observation of scientific possibilities in war. In itself it is not a weapon but a no-game condition. It is then a personal menace to you and me by concentrating the attention of governments upon itself and leaving us wide open to anything.

Any nation that creates one of these interim weapons with everybody defending against nothing but atomic bombs could cast an empire across the face of earth with the greatest of ease, with no opposition anywhere.

The future of our race depends upon a continued fluid alertness on the part of a government into all branches of science and a complete and continuous good communication line to scientists such as doctors of medicine, nuclear physicists and Scientologists to discover what is known, being done and what we can do. Then our answer to the whole problem is that we could tell what could be done scientifically. There IS something that the governments of Earth can do.

I don't say that anybody will effect this, or that we ourselves will bring any pressure to bear in any direction, but there is one thing that they all can do and that is *to become more civilized.*

LECTURE THREE

Radiation and Scientology

In this lecture I will deal with radiation and Scientology. There are a number of things which have been learned during the past year and a half in Scientology which directly relate to radiation and it would be a great shame not to make these things known to the public at this time.

We already have data of sufficient importance and reliability to demonstrate that the Scientologist by processing and by processing of others can very easily nullify many of the dangers to a person of such a thing as a polluted atmosphere.

We care very little about whether there is radiation in the atmosphere because a person who is in excellent physical condition does not particularly suffer mentally and thus physically from the effects of radiation. When a person is at a level where his general physical health is good, then this worry is not capable of depressing him into ill health. Radiation is more of a mental than a physical problem and Scientology handles that.

The factors in Scientology which are most definitely influenced by radiation are the factors which are most definitely influenced by life. When we try to divide a peculiar illness from the general illnesses of being alive we are at once in conflict with the fact that man is as well as he is well. If each one of the infinite number of factors which can make him ill had to be taken up separately and independently and distinctly with an entirely different treatment, we would discover ourselves with our noses always and forever stuck into the newest and latest disease.

We don't do that although we are aware of the latest techniques. It is an interesting fact that the latest technique always runs out the earlier technique—and that is why it is the latest technique. We are not studying the latest disease. We are studying a method to eradicate the cures of former times and the nullification of processes which were used earlier.

A technique is as good as it runs out earlier techniques. The technique which runs out, eradicates or even throws into restimulation an older technique is senior to it.

Let's assume that we are treating smallpox. We find at first that we inject a serum which makes the individual's arm swell up, makes them feel ill and feverish. After that they do or don't get smallpox.

After further investigation and research we find that we could refine and perfect this technique by giving it orally. This seems to have a good workability. Finally we discover something that has to do with a particular hot bath, if you can imagine such a cure, and find that if we give somebody a hot bath he won't get smallpox.

The technique of the three which is senior to the others will run out the other two. It is quite interesting that if the hot bath technique was a good pervasive, sweeping technique and was a considerable improvement on the other two, when we put the man in the hot bath, he would at once feel sick in his stomach from the pill and his arm would tend to get swollen from the old injection. After that the pill and injection would not trouble him any longer.

Yesterday's Cure Is Today's Disease

That doesn't happen often in physical medicine, but it is not unknown. With the Scientologist we see this phenomenon often during our handling of people. It is highly probable that man has had cures along the developing genetic line which have become the diseases of tomorrow and if we can solve the factor of the cure that becomes the disease—which, by the way we have solved in Scientology—we are then capable of this kind of curing.

Alcohol as a Medicine

Let's take alcohol as an example.

Alcohol was once the greatest medicine that man had. It was a wonderful medicine. If anything happened to a man from snake bite to a love affair, any disease, in fact, we administrated alcohol. That was a cure, but now we have alcoholism.

It is interesting that only a century and a half ago the stores of a British man-of-war amounted in terms of weight to more than 50% alcoholic beverages and less than 50% food and other amenities. Alcohol was quite a tremendous thing.

But here is an oddity. Today alcohol makes one tired. It has been laid in on the genetic line evidently to such a degree that it now produces the illness which it was most used as a remedy for. Any time one got tired one took a drink. In past years we conceive that the genetic blueprint is marching along and that it accumulates experiences.

It is definitely in the realm of genetics, but the geneticist has never realized that the experience the body line has in one generation, may culminate in another generation. Darwin found that if you took horses up to the high country in the Middle East they would grow long hair after a season or two. When they were taken back into the low hot country, they wouldn't get rid of the long hair for about four generations. It tells us that the genetic line does carry a memory of what happened. There are many proofs and incidents of this character.

Very few people have added this into the field of medicine, taking it out of the line of natural selection. Today a person may get tired when he takes a drink. In other words, it restimulates that which it was once made to cure. Possibly on the genetic line, some time or another, and being farfetched about it, radiation might have been a cure for something. Using this principle that the cure eventually becomes the disease and eventually restimulates the disease it is supposed to cure, I am sure that somewhere on the genetic line, radiation was used to cure a bad stomach or skin. It certainly is today—sunbathing.

The Sun Is a Ball of Radiation

What is the sun but a ball of radiation? There are photons that come from the sun but they are hand in glove with a great deal of other radiation. Radiation is all over the atmosphere, always has been. Sunburn is not an overdose of heat but simply radiation.

In my basic physics textbook they used to teach that the sun was combusting on hydrogen. They calculated the length of life of the sun on hydrogen, but if that were so one would get a difference in the heat of the sun from year to year because it would be burning out. It was an interesting fact that the sun didn't burn out so the theory was eventually abandoned and people finally owned up and said that they didn't know why the sun kept on burning. It was only when nuclear physics became dominant in men's thinking that sunlight was explained, and sunlight is now understood to be occasioned by a continuous fission going on a sphere called the sun. Therefore sunburn is a radiation burn.

Sunburn and Radiation Burns

When one looks at people who are burned in an atomic blast such as there was at Hiroshima, one is looking at the outer fringes of burns that look very much like sunburn.

For instance, a man was standing with his back to a picket fence. The bomb exploded far back of him and he had sunburn where there weren't any pickets. In other words he got a burn pattern much as one would if one was wearing a bathing costume.

If radiation is drifting around in the air all the time, one is not getting a direct burn, one is getting a sort of continuous intolerable type of burn which is too imbalanced and the absorption of which one doesn't find healthy. Every person has a great deal of experience with sunburn on the genetic line and sunburn occasionally causes hives, red flushes, prickliness, an upset stomach and colitis. It will even cause loss of hair. It is something with which we have had experience. Radiation is not new and strange. There is just more of it and it is drifting in the wrong place.

X-rays

We have also had X-rays. X-rays oddly enough has been used as a cure for cancer. A cure for cancer? It must have been in vogue for some time for the excellent reason that X-ray can cause cancer. It is therefore no surprise that if one tries to cure something long enough and often enough, it may eventually cause what it is trying to cure. Its effectiveness will diminish.

We therefore must handle this cure factor, which we can do with the technology we have in Scientology.

The Solution of a Problem

In other words, the solution of a problem is the problem, not a solution. If one wants no liability in any solution then its solution is the problem.

Somebody decides that his wife is mad and he takes her to see a psychiatrist. They put big electrodes on her head and shock her and she comes back. What is she suffering from now? She is suffering from being electrocuted. So one day she walks over to the light and as she turns it on it short-circuits, gives her a slight shock and she is crazy all over again. It often happens and it is quite common. They are using electricity in some wild, barbaric manner in some offhanded attempt to cure insanity.

The Solution Is Always the Problem

This business of curing illnesses carries with it the liability of leaving the cure sitting there. We cure some disease by running an individual's temperature to 107 degrees Fahrenheit and leaving it there for 48 hours. A few years go by and something is wrong with him. What is wrong with him? Well, he gets hot!

104

One therefore has to have the individual conceive of problems of comparable magnitude to the problem in order to take his fixation off the problem. As long as he is fixated on the problem and then solves it he continues to be fixated on the problem. He just puts a barrier between himself and the problem but the problem is still there.

One therefore has to raise the individual's tolerance for that type of problem and the moment that is done, the problem is "solved". In other words, the solution is always the problem. One has to be able to "handle," "tolerate" and "confront" the problem. When one cannot confront a problem and one "solves" it completely he then becomes obsessed with the solution of it.

Let's take a look at radiation. People cannot solve it, cannot confront it—I should say they cannot confront it as it is drifting all through the atmosphere. Have somebody look into space for a while. One says to him, "Don't look at *anything*. Just look into space," and after a while this person is in rather poor condition. He will get queasy.

Therefore if radiation is scattered all through the air and we tell people: "Look, it is floating all around in space, but you cannot see it," everybody starts getting queasy. We can produce to a marked degree all the effects of radiation in Scientology with the greatest of ease simply by restimulation and in the absence of any real radiation!

One can be made to relive a past experience and therefore can be made to relive past illnesses as *Dianetics: The Modern Science of Mental Health* has demonstrated. One can actually see people stuck in these moments of illnesses.

If a person is liable to get restimulated or is upset by dangers in the atmosphere, he will get sick in his stomach a short while after one has asked him to look into space. One gets colitis and gastroenteritis often as a result of this apparently harmless technique of asking people to look into space without paying particular notice to any specific objects that may be present. This is a test anybody could make.

Pollution of Spaces Makes Effect Out of Man

Pollution of and danger in space makes a total effect out of man and one is brought to believe one can do nothing about it. These are the combinations from our viewpoint as Scientologists, which bring this condition we know as radiation sickness and we can do something about each one of them. We can give man something to confront that is like radiation and being able to confront this we give him practice in confronting the unconfrontable.

The Other Factors behind Radiation

What are the other factors behind radiation? Radiation is being used as a control mechanism. It is being used to control people. They are not supposed to

106

have war with and are to obey countries that do have radiation.

As it goes on it becomes apparent to people that it is a control mechanism.

Control

As long as a person is allergic to control he will suffer from attempts to control him. If everybody has an allergy to control and to being controlled, and thinks that there is something wrong with control, isn't that an aberration? Isn't that something that should be handled by a Scientologist—something one should raise the tolerance of people on? People get so afraid of being controlled that they resist everything. When they get afraid of radiation when it is used as a control mechanism, they resist it and it burns them — and only then does it burn them.

One can conduct this experiment by taking somebody and saying: "Isn't it terrible about this radiation. Think of all the air round here in this room at this moment being full of little invisible particles that are just chewing our bodies to bits." He gets the idea and wonders why he is itching all over his body.

Resistance to Control

If people are allergic to control it is something that they ought to settle with themselves. A person can only be controlled against his will as long he is allergic to control and it is against his will. A person who is very bland about this subject and doesn't mind being controlled can be controlled as easily as a toy and can stop it as easily as a giant. He has power of choice over control and if one has power of choice over control it doesn't much matter if one is being controlled or controlling a situation or persons oneself.

As long as control, directions, orders and postulates are resisted, a person has a tendency to lock up with them—in other words become their effect which then produces a considerable discomfort to the person. Resistance to a terminal—person or object—brings about one way or another a closure of terminals with the thing to such a degree that an individual then obeys it, doesn't know he is obeying it or what he is obeying and that is more or less what aberration is.

Radiation and Control

If radiation is used as a control factor then a person is made to close terminals with something which his body cannot tolerate. But it is the *person* who is closing that terminal, *not* the body, and that is our foremost discovery. As long as we have an orientation on the subject of radiation, are no longer resisting it, or upset about it, and particularly if we are in fair condition with regard to space, spaciousness and don't get claustrophobia, then we really don't have to fear from radiation. That is the first thing we have learned in Scientology.

This organization of Scientologists knows a great deal about radiation, since it was once in Arizona, 250 miles from a hundred and some atomic bomb tests that were made in Nevada. The central headquarters of this organization were moved from Phoenix, Arizona to Washington, D.C., only because pianos began to count like uranium mines. Everything was live and radioactive. Dust blew in one's face at night and one had sunburn although there was no sun. There was just too much radiation.

We had a lot of experience and found something rather peculiar. We found that people who were in good condition were not in restimulation with regard to radiation and those who were in bad condition would get something that would hardly count on a geiger counter and would get sick in their stomaches. people received Scientological processing—"treatment"—and had no further repercussion from radiation.

Here is a good example. A man came into the Hubbard Scientology Organization in Phoenix. He had been driving past one of the atomic bomb explosion sites and as he went past the site at some considerable distance away, he saw the flash on the horizon. At once his face and eyes swelled and he could hardly drive into Phoenix. He was in terrible condition and felt very bad about this. So I just gave him a Scientology assist and the swelling went down immediately.

The general auditing of individuals is then a basic solution. Group auditing also solves the control factor and helps communication to a marked degree.

Radiation and Scientology Processing

The reaction to radiation in persons who have been given Scientology processing is by actual tests much lower than those who have not received it. We have conducted some experiments in that direction. But even we would find it very difficult and even antipathetic to get everybody together and give them the amount of group processing needed as safeguard against radiation.

Is there anything that we could give a person that would help him against radiation? There is. There are several preparations which prevent radiation. It is getting rather common now and progress is being made on the whole subject. Here is an article from "The New Scientist" of the 28th March, 1957, by Dr. Peter Alexander, called "Protection against Radiation."

He tells us that, working independently, several people have found that harmful effects of radiation can be reduced by injecting some quite simple chemicals before exposure to the rays. The comment on the whole article is: "Could medicines be used to protect against the effects of radiation?"

A short time ago such a suggestion would have been thought absurd. Today chemical protection against radiation is a subject of much research.

Dianazene

But we are leading on this. We knew that old-time nicotinic acid restimulated and ran out sunburns and that a person who had been given nicotinic acid actually did not receive a continuous effect from it. Anybody can make this test.

It happens that there is an incorrect entry in both the British and American pharmacopoeias. It says that nicotinic acid—not niacinamide—turns on a flush, and in overdose is therefore toxic. This is not correct. People who have taken nicotinic acid in overdoses do get red and prickly but one has to take about 90 grains to kill oneself.

It is fascinating that there could be this insufficient information. It could be that people don't look because that isn't what it does at all. In a large number of cases it doesn't turn on flushes but turns on hives, gastroenteritis, aching bones, or a fearful, terrified condition which is not a physical reaction at all. Here is a variable reaction from something toxic— and notice that it turns on the conditions brought about by atomic radiation.

What sort of a toxic pill is this which when administered over a period of time is no longer toxic even though all the time it is being administered it is above toleration? The body cannot tolerate the amount that is being administered but after a while it no longer has any effect. Unless one knows Dianetics

111

and Scientology this doesn't seem to make much sense.

Nicotinic acid runs out, abolishes, sunburns—and that is the simple answer to this question. When it is given to a person, he gets sunburns he has already had before and turns as red as a beet. Keep him on a regimented dose every day and after a while two things will happen: one, he no longer gets sick when nicotinic acid is administered to him and, two, he doesn't have a bad reaction from sunburn.

We have made the test with sunlamps and found that a person's liability to being burned is decreased by the administration of nicotinic acid and the running out of past burns. This, therefore, is true of this type of radiation illness.

I conducted several experiments in 1950 which were in total disagreement with the pharmacopoeia, but any medical doctor or biochemist could make the same experiments. One would administer 200 mg nicotinic acid per day to somebody and see all the manifestations I have spoken earlier, turn on, eventually disappear and not recur until one has administered about 500 mg per day, which will turn it all on again, but much less this time. Then one gives this person 1,000 mg per day for several days and finds that there is just a small reaction after which one administers 2,000 mg per day and finds no more effects. One can thus feed people this toxic drug without any effect whatsoever.

Remembering this series of experiments I made in 1950 I again looked them up in the files of the Hubbard Dianetic Research Foundation. More recently we got some brave volunteer who took nicotinic acid over a period of a couple of weeks and sure enough our old experiments were bearing out with one exception: the reactions per dose were five and six times more violent than they had been in 1950!

I then got hold of some of the people who were given nicotinic acid in 1950 and they took the same course all over again. They got a little sick in their stomachs but were better off than other people and they got an entirely different reaction.

In order to make the intake of nicotinic acid more effective, I did more experimenting and eventually combined it with vitamins and other minerals and finally produced a formula called Dianazene.

The Formula for Dianazene

Nicotinic Acid. . . . . . . 200 mg.
Iron Ferrous Gluconate . . . 10 grains.
Vitamin B_1. . . . . 25 mg.
Vitamin B_2 — Riboflavin . . . 50 mg.
Vitamin C—Ascorbic Acid . 200 to 500 mg.
Dicalcium Phosphate . . . . . 15 to 20 grains.

It should be taken daily, all at the same time, with milk and chocolate.

But it is not the best solution. It is a cure. It does

something and it can eventually be run out with Scientology. But if we didn't have anything else Dianazene might serve the purpose very well in a limited sense.

Dianazene runs out radiation—or what appears to be radiation. It also proofs a person up against radiation in some degree. I have seen it run out skin cancer. A man who didn't have much liability to skin cancer (only had a few moles) took Dianazene. His whole jaw turned into a raw mass of cancer. He kept on taking Dianazene and it disappeared after a while. I was looking at a case of cancer that might have happened.

There is another instance of somebody who had a little bit of colitis which worried him slightly from time to time. After taking Dianazene he started to bleed from the intestines. He kept on taking this formula and came out without colitis. He may have been facing an eventual colitis of a fatal nature— hemorrhages.

The whole point in taking Dianazene is to keep taking it until bad effects vanish.

As the level of food intake from country to country varies, it is important that people who don't eat regular wholesome food take milk and chocolate with this preparation, otherwise they get a very poor reaction to it. I found that if one took milk and chocolate with it—or milk and glucose—it worked much better. In other words, the people who are the poorest fed would evidently be the most susceptible to radiation.

However, there could be thousands of other factors involved. If we are alert there is no reason to worry about radiation at this time particularly. But there is the same old worry about the case and health level of the peoples of the Earth, and if we continue along in this same direction, we would also win in the face of radiation. Who knows that we wouldn't get a plague tomorrow that would wipe out nations. I assure you that it would be the people who are worried and are in a bad state of health who would go down first.

If one wanted to get the better of the plague, whether man or bug made, one should be audited by Scientology technologies. That seems to me about all I could say offhand that one might find of use in the understanding and handling of atomic radiation.

Man's Real Enemies

The whole subject of atomic fission is a subject of violence. It isn't true that every new scientific development carries with it several martyrs, but atomic fission does because its first use was in war for the slaughter of men, women and children at Hiroshima. It has carried with it a considerable reputation, but our position as Scientologists is very sharp and clear and I have spoken about the two important factors which I will mention again.

Point number one is: *The greatest danger of atomic fission and the testing of bombs is the hysteria it can cause amongst populaces, a hysteria which can grow so great that a populace can be thrown out of control*; and point number two: *The people who suffer from small doses of radiation are people who have a bad health record*, who are not in excellent mental and physical condition.

It is possible to take somebody who is in excellent mental and physical condition and give him enough dosage to make him extremely ill, but it is my understanding of this that the people who are hit are the infirm, the old, those who are liable to various shocks and upsets in life anyway.

This factor has not been covered by atomic energy releases since it is not much investigated except by ourselves. Therefore, concluding the second point, those people who are in excellent condition and whose mental stability is beyond question, need have little fear of this particular test cloud that goes around the world at this time.

Under the heading of number one, a Scientologist by group auditing is capable of bringing a considerable calmness into an area which is upset, and under point number two, it is the business of a Scientologist to place people into a level of existence where they don't get sick from every stray germ that wanders their way. This is one of our goals. Therefore these two points are completely germane to Scientology.

The Harmful Effects of X-rays

X-rays are fully as deadly as atomic fission. A repeated continuous application of X-rays to a person can bring about anything and everything that atomic fission brings about on a test pollution of the atmosphere level. It certainly brings about a condition of high count in the individual if many X-rays are taken, so that if he gets a little more X-ray or radiation fallout, he is liable to become ill. Ordinarily X-rays are applied to sick people!

The Genetic Aspects of the Atomic Bomb

As far as the genetic aspects of the atomic bomb are concerned, this is, of course, where everybody's attention is centering because sex is still so secret in our Anglo-American society of 1957. It is a good thing that we are not living in Victorian times, because we would not dare mention the fact that our children are going to be born with their legs coming out of their ears. It is still sufficiently secret to pin people's attention to the genetic aspects of radiation. These are of least importance and are of no great consequence at this time.

The mortality rate of babies a century ago because of puerperal fever was, by percentage, a hundred times higher than is the rate of deformities due to radiation. The percentage of deformities and blindness caused by bad midwifery and poor medical practice a century and a half ago surpasses the radiation figures and if anybody wants to be shocked about it, let him be shocked about the way it was then, not the way it is going to be. Of course, it is upsetting to think of a hundred million populace having several thousands congenital idiots simply because of testing. But how about the people who are already born and grown up who will become ill, ineffective and die? That is a more important fact. Testing *at its present rate* isn't going to spoil completely the genetic line.

I was visiting a hospital some time ago and came

118

across a girl who had had a baby about ten to twelve days before. She had stayed several days beyond when they would ordinarily dismiss her. She was lying in a very inert position, looking very sad. I asked her doctor what the matter was and he told me that there was there was nothing the matter but that the child was only surrounded by half the placenta in the womb. Something had happened in the growth of the child that whereas the baby was all right, only half the placenta developed. This was a malformation and the woman believed that something was wrong with her due to this development of the placenta. This so deprived her of her usual spirits that she lay there not recovering.

I became very interested in this as I know that X-rays disarrange the genes and the placenta is represented in the genes. If one of these genes is deranged one gets such a thing as half a placenta.

I was thinking in terms of all the radiation that was in this area as they were blowing up bomb after bomb about 250 miles away. Theoretically it could have been those bombs that were causing her genetic upset.

So I asked her: "What does your husband do?" thinking possibly that he was one of the people who was associated with the tests. She told me, however, that he was a radiologist, an X-ray technician. I then asked her what duty he was performing nine months ago and after a while she groaned her answer which was that her husband was taking a special course of training on new X-ray equipment at a certain military hospital nearby and for six days was doing nothing else but setting up and using the most powerful X-ray equipment extant.

This woman fortunately was well educated and I said, "Did it ever occur to you that it might not be your fault that only half a placenta developed?" From that moment her interest in life returned and she left hospital that afternoon unable to wait to confront her husband with this discovery.

Here was a certainty that the testing of atomic bombs 250 miles away did not cause the disarrangement in the case of this particular woman. Her husband, being an X-ray technician, had been on a spree of X-ray training and his own genes had been badly disarranged by the X-ray equipment and his use of it.

People do pick out an assumed cause for something and it is fashion to blame it for all that cannot be explained satisfactorily. Radiation is loose in the world and everything then is assigned to radiation. People do this fixedly.

Wrong Assignment of Causes

Many more things should be assigned to radiation at this moment than are being assigned to it. People are not at all aware of the tremendous effect that this testing will have and the low morale that it will give people.

However, people will assign more and more things to radiation and just about the time when they are assigning about enough, somebody will say that they must not do so and prohibit them from doing so. They will obsessively start assigning things to it until somebody starts jailing people for causing hysteria. After that people will start misassigning and assigning on a dispersal anything to everything and it will no longer make sense. People will no longer be capable of assigning actual cause, and then there will be chaos.

The thing to do is to be factual about it and say that just certain things are assignable to radiation. Assign them, take them in stride and the government would do extremely well to work along with organizations such as the Scientologist. One should do what one can about them. Publish this data rather widely, showing that the necessary steps that can be taken are being taken and be factual about it the whole way. One shouldn't try to play it down, but be factual and go on from there, not only trying to do something about radiation but also the many things that make life all but impossible for people. Shortage of food can be much more fatal than alarm on radiation.

The Problem of the Middle East

Right now the starved condition of the Arab, his slave condition—a mental condition that tells him he can't

121

have anything—makes it impossible for the Middle East to exist peacefully. Large responsible nations have tried to do something about the Middle East. They will never be able to do anything about the Middle East until they have solved this "below poverty" status of the Arab. The Arabs have been pushed down since the days of Chaldea. The history of the Middle East is one of extreme oppression and slavery. Something has to come along to undo those years of slavery so that the people within themselves can feel enough security to work, win and survive in this universe. That is a very worthy project.

There is just one group on Earth at this moment that could do anything about the mental and thus the political state of the Middle East and that is the Scientologist. We know that a person can be placed so low that he cannot "have." If one tries to give him anything he will just tear it up. We know that the Arab will continue to make nothing out of anything he runs into the Middle East so long as his poverty is continued and confirmed.

That appears to be a very interesting and more worthwhile international project since the entire area sews up one of the great waterways of Earth, which has already caused international upset to the United States and England.

The condition of the Arab populaces is based on the fact that back through the years many people have had a hand in placing the populaces in that area in a condition where they can never win. One of these people was Genghis Khan. How would you like to have this tyrant, who made a pyramid of skulls at every crossroad, as your ruler for a generation or six? There was Tamerlane and Bayazid the Thunderbolt of the Ottoman Turk, conqueror after conqueror, nothing but oppression and iron heels. This has amounted to an impossible political problem unless it is entered at the level of the individual.

A Scientologist can group process these Arabs to a level where they can be made capable to take some aid and assistance. One would educate some Arabs up to a point where they could group process very well and then let them process their people towards survival.

The cost of such a program would actually be the cost of about one volley of shells from a fleet.

The Problem of India

India is another country where the people are so downtrodden that they are in a state where they "can't have," "can't own." One cannot even govern these people any more. Anybody who goes in to govern India has great difficulty because the people are below the point of no return by past technologies. They are all directed in the direction of slavery — Brahmanism, for example. Here is an international problem of great importance to the world, which cries for solution.

Man's First Enemy Is Man

First among man's enemies is man. Because man does more in one war than all the bugs of Africa have ever done.

Man's inhumanity to man was a subject which was addressed with the philosophy of Jesus of Nazareth. But Christianity has not stopped war. It has done a lot of good in this world but it has not stopped war. Unless man can stop this international insanity one will see this thing called radiation, the hydrogen bomb and the guided missile used by some country against us all and itself at the same time.

It is all very well to say that nobody will use it. Just about the time when somebody is losing an Adolf Hitler or somebody of that ilk says: "Press button A." Button A is wired up to a lot of guided missiles and requires only one man's decision to destroy an entire continent, to poison the atmosphere so thoroughly that man vanishes from this planet.

The Real Danger

The real danger is not radiation. The true danger is man's uncivilized state. Unless something can come along and cure him of his barbarism he is not going to survive. He has many enemies if he really wants enemies. The locust of Africa, the various fevers of India and the hail storms of Kansas are enemies. Why focus on radiation? If man is to survive he must first be capable of facing his enemies—and those enemies aren't man. He just thinks they are. Until man can be brought to face his true enemies on Earth, he cannot really be considered to be a civilized being, because he is fighting the wrong targets.

The Worthwhile Projects Are Neglected Because of War

How man, making such slow progress on every other frontier, can waste time to turn around and fight his brother is appalling. The Sahara Desert could be put under cultivation and that would straighten out some of the economic situations in that area. This would require far more effort than was put into the North African Campaigns but it could be done. It would have to be carefully planned. He already was making progress in this direction before World War II came into being and retarded the little progress he had already made.

One cannot keep overrunning an area with the terror of war and its destruction and decide that anything is going to survive in that area. Man has a madness and that madness is called war. That madness hasn't really anything to do with politics.

Most people who go into a long chant about how one outlaws war are saying that we must suppress national governments. That is the last thing I would ever advise. The truth is very simple. A government becomes worried about its ability to control its populace and neighbors, and resorts to war as a means of compelling obedience at home as well as abroad.

In actuality a weakness and insecurity of government causes war. If a government were very strong and felt secure it would employ the most peaceful quiet methods of granting beingness and getting co-operation from its potential enemies. It wouldn't fight a war. One doesn't find an educated secure man fighting with his neighbors. No, the person who fights his neighbors is a very insecure, not at all sane man.

War Begets War

To bring about peace it is not enough to suppress and smash down every single government in the world. That is just emotion in the wrong direction. That is how wars are caused. After the blood bath of the French Revolution, France was in a continuous wars for decades. In other words, she was fairly well at peace as long as she had a king and a fairly strong government. When that government was turned over to Robespierres and Napoleons there was a continuous state of war.

To have nullified the tremendous wasteful efforts of France and all the suffering which pursued those various wars, it would have been necessary to bolster the French government, not weaken it. As long as every nation is upset about every other nation and as long as any nation refuses to bolster and strengthen its neighbor nations, then war remains a threat.

If the United States were willing to grant beingness to the various other great nations of the world, and if they were willing to grant beingness to her, one would see a security mounting up which would practically make war impossible. But these countries are still doing something which is quite wrong. They are weakening the government of Russia.

The Trouble with Russia

The trouble with Russia is that its government is weak. Its government has been overthrown by revolution and has been a threat to world peace ever since. Just as France became an international menace in 1790. The Russian revolution never should have happened. But the conditions of Russia never should have happened either. In other words, the non-civilized condition of Russia, its unenlightened state for the last many centuries directly resulted in this threat we call Russia today.

We are not implying that we should throw everything overboard and admit communism. The truth of the matter is that communism is a losing philosophy. It was invented in Germany a century ago and is a German philosophy, and the Germans thought it was an idiotic doctrine and they threw it out. The Germans are not buying it now even though Russia is forcing it upon them.

Regardless of any political philosophy, unless Russia and its satellites can prosper in one way or the other, they will continue to be a "have not" nation. Maybe these people are a "have not" people like the Arab in the Middle East and if that is the case, then sooner or later we will find ourselves at war with Russia.

The Answer to the Atomic Bomb

The answer to the atomic bomb does not lie in the field of "there shall be no further development in the field of the atomic bomb." We all know that if a war weapon exists it will be used some time. *The answer to the atomic bomb lies in the change of status of man and his national governments.* These governments must be stronger and people must co-operate with them. They must be strengthened and the peoples of those nations must be addressed realistically and brought up to a point where they can feel some security, where they can *have* something, exist themselves at peace with their own neighbors and only then have we solved the problem of the atomic bomb. All the atomic bomb is doing is catalyzing the necessity for this solution.

If a technology exists which can bring a higher level of civilization to man, then that technology should be used to the utmost to advance that state of civilization. It should not be used to destroy or decry governments, to propagandize or pull the rug out from underneath the men who are trying. It should be used to bring about stronger, more secure governments and more civilized populaces.

128

The Turn of the Road

We are at a turn of the road. Man before could almost afford to go in a state of barbarism. Today he cannot afford his bestiality, his inhumanity to his neighbors, for many reasons not the least of which is that the next war will be the last war. One really shouldn't worry about the next war. It will be over in twenty minutes. But we should try to make that war unnecessary.

Britain's Nuclear Reactors

The Electricity Board in Britain is doing a wonderful job. It has just constructed 47 new power stations and is now constructing twelve reactor stations. This is a peacetime use of atomic fission and Britain is the first to dedicate herself to employing atomic fission to the assistance of man and his works as we have already seen in Calder Hall.

This has not received great publicity throughout the world. There is no great news story connected with this. Britain, the leader in these reactor projects, is planning to use atomic fission to put hundreds of millions more kilowatts up and down the length and breadth of the land and thus supply the power which has been wanting.

It would be of great interest in the United States and would certainly be food for thought to those who say that they must build more bombs.

129

One ought to know that atomic fission can be used for peace and would not thereafter throw poison such as gamma rays into the air.

How a Reactor Works

The Electricity Board's offices in London, W.1, carry a tremendous number of billboards and bulletin boards concerning this particular project. A reactor can be explained as simply as this: It is a massive container which contains such elements that give off gamma, such as radium, uranium, which are placed in the container. A lid is put on the container and a small hole is bored in the side of the container. An electronic machine gun is focused on the small piece of uranium. When one of the electrons of the machine gun hits the uranium, it knocks off a bursting particle. In other words, it causes a fission to occur which generates heat. Added to this container are a number of steam pipes and a channel which goes over to an ordinary steam engine which returns the condensed water back into the pipes and system. The water comes back from the steam engine, going again through the container. The electronic machine gun shoots an electron, the water is heated by the small explosion, which is very hot and then goes over, runs the steam engine which drives an ordinary generator. This generator is connected with a transformer which puts electricity in the wires and somebody miles away weaves cotton from the power.

There is no danger of such fission getting out of control since there isn't really sufficient fissionable material present to cause much damage. One can even bombard lower order elements and so we are not even dependent on a continuous supply of uranium to make these projects possible. What is an industrial system but a great deal of cheap power?

Automation

People in Britain are worried about automation. They are worried that this will throw them out of work. If people work, they must have something to buy. There must be something to buy for the money one possesses as money is just as good as one can buy something with it and as bad as one cannot.

Money is something that can be converted into product. Supposing one had a workman's idea of a wonderful civilization whereby everybody did piece work all by himself and was paid abundantly for it. What is he going to do with this great amount of money if he cannot buy piece work which is not available?

A workman certainly ought to have a radio, a decent home well furnished. His children ought to have good clothes and there ought to be wholesome food on the table. He should have a motor car to take him places. He believes this whether he is a Spaniard, Frenchman or American. But if these commodities don't get manufactured in sufficient numbers to make them cheap nobody is going to have them and that is a point which he overlooks. Automation must be present in this society. There must be something that can produce enough so that man can have enough.

Our present society is existing on a small per cent of its workers. The potential workers in society are being diverted in so many directions on a non-productive level such as war weapons. Every time one builds war weapons one has just expended workers, and everything it takes to support these workers. One has to have automation in order to make up for the loss—and that takes fuel.

If a nation is going to be successful, it has got to have raw products, fuel and willing workers. Get short of one of these three and it will not be successful.

The Willing Worker

The South American nations have more raw products and more fuel, but less willing workers than most nations. But people are still running around in loin cloths, carrying bows and arrows. They have the fuel and raw materials but not the willing worker.

If all the workmen in America and England became unwilling to work, one would again see a barbarism. We in Scientology could prevent such unwillingness rather easily. We have taken that up and solved it in *The Problems of Work*.

One can orient a person with regard to work and make him brace up to it and have a good time whereas he has been avoiding work before—we can restore his lost willingness. If anything kills the Anglo-American society, it will either die under tremendous political blunders which bring about an atomic war, or this philosophy that work is too hard to confront. This philosophy of "We must all retire some day" amounts to "our greatest ambition is to do nothing." That idea is one of our greatest enemies.

This is how this state of mind is created: A man is having a good time building, let us say, a bird cage. Somebody comes along and says to him: "Aren't you tired? You're working so hard. I should think that after a long day at the office you would feel worn out and would be incapable of going on any further." This man was enjoying building a bird cage. The next day somebody criticizes him at the office about his work and he feels tired.

Tiredness is willingness gone bad. People who are willing don't get tired. It is only when something makes man unwilling, stops him too often and kills his interest in what he is doing, that he becomes exhausted.

People have to be told and kept in the frame of mind that life is worth living and that things are worth doing. If governments and civilizations continue to produce things to convince people that they are just slaves and that things aren't worth doing and that they have to be pushed into work with a whip, the whole society degenerates.

No society can exist on a fabric of slaves. Those that have, have died: Greece, Rome, Germany. A society can only survive when it is built by the shoulders and hands of willing men. Governments should take this into account. They do with social security, health programs, etc., but they can do more about it.

The things I've mentioned in this lecture are more important than radiation. Man's inhumanity to man has always been present. He has always been able to reach over and put his hand on a deadly and diabolical weapon. Whether that weapon was a club with a knot at the end of it, a tower musket, a new high-powered super velocity bazooka, or a guided missile with an atomic bomb in it, remember that it was handled by a man who is being inhuman to men. Therefore the solving of the atomic bomb would not prevent atomic warfare.

Helping the Governments of Earth

A government will always accept a helping hand but it is so scarce that it takes a government leader a long time to be convinced that it is being held out. So few people help the government that they don't know what the hand is out for. Men use governments to feather their own nests and better their own ends, but there are sincere men in government who are trying to do what is right.

If we wish to go any direction in the field of

politics, let's be sure we go in the direction of giving the existing government and the powers that be a hand in bringing about a higher level of civilization and a better understanding of life. If we strike at anything we should strike at these intermediate problems such as the atomic bomb, smallpox, whooping cough, bubonic plague and all the rest of the things that confront man as his enemies.

What do we have in Scientology with which to help man and governments? We have something which assists man, not something that fights man's enemies. Man will fight his real enemies which he isn't fighting now.

Our job as Scientologists in this society is to bring man up to a level where he can confront his natural enemies and live at peace with his fellows, and if we can do that on a very broad level as we are doing in a smaller sphere, then we would have brought a better civilization to Earth—and that I think, is what we are trying to do. Thank you.

*   *   *   *

The interests of the Hubbard College of Scientology (Church of Scientology of California) in radiation are only these:—

It creates widespread hysteria;
Scientology can handle hysteria.

It creates physical disabilities;
Scientology can help prevent them.

Scientology is the principal agency that is helping to prevent radiation disabilities in people at this time.

The radiation count of Earth has not been increased by bomb testing. The anguish of Earth has been multiplied by bomb terror. You can survive with Scientology.

CONCLUSION

The Aims of Scientology

A civilization without insanity, without criminals and without war, where the able can prosper and honest beings can have rights, and where Man is free to rise to greater heights, are the aims of Scientology.

First announced to an enturbulated world twenty-eight years ago, these aims are well within the grasp of our technology.

Nonpolitical in nature, Scientology welcomes any individual of any creed, race or nation.

We seek no revolution. We seek only evolution to higher states of being for the individual and for society.

We are achieving our aims.

After endless millenia of ignorance about himself, his mind and the universe, a breakthrough has been made for Man.

Other efforts Man has made have been surpassed.

The combined truths of fifty thousand years of thinking men, distilled and amplified by new discoveries about Man, have made for this success.

We welcome you to Scientology. We only expect of you your help in achieving our aims and helping others. We expect you to be helped.

Scientology is the most vital movement on Earth today.

In a turbulent world, the job is not easy. But then, if it were, we wouldn't have to be doing it.

We respect Man and believe he is worthy of help. We respect you and believe you, too, can help.

Scientology does not owe its help. We have done nothing to cause us to propitiate. Had we done so, we would not now be bright enough to do what we are doing.

Man suspects all offers of help. He has often been betrayed, his confidence shattered. Too frequently he has given his trust and been betrayed. We may err, for we build a world with broken straws. But we will never betray your faith in us so long as you are one of us.

The sun never sets on Scientology.

And may a new day dawn for you, for those you love and for Man.

Our aims are simple, if great.

And we will succeed, and are succeeding at each new revolution of the Earth.

Your help is acceptable to us.

Our help is yours.

BIBLIOGRAPHY

Notes on Atomic Energy for Medical Officers. H.M.S.O. 1955.

Nuclear Weapons. (Civil Defense Manual Vol. I.) H.M.S.O. 1956.

Concepts of Radiological Health. Ingraham, Terrill and Moeller. U.S. Department of Health, Education and Wellfare 1954.

The Biological Effects of Atomic Radiation. Summary reports of the U.S. National Academy of Sciences 1956.

Continental Weapon Tests ... Public Safety. U.S. Atomic Energy Commission 1953.

The Effects of High-Yield Nuclear Explosions. U.S. Atomic Energy Commission.

Preliminary Report of the International Medical Commission on the effects on human health of Atomic and Hydrogen Bomb explosions. World Congress of Doctors. Vienna 1955.

"The Bombs." Sevitt. *The Lancet* p. 187. July 23rd, 1955.

"Radio-Active Poisons." Schubert. *Scientific American*. August 1955.

Federation of American Scientists; Newsletter ... July 9th, 1956.

"Protection against Radiation." Alexander. *The New Scientist*. March 28th, 1957.

"The Hazard of Strontium 90." *The New Scientist*. March 28th, 1957.

Hiroshima. John Hersey. Penguin.

About L. Ron Hubbard

L. Ron Hubbard was born in Tilden, Nebraska, on 13 March, 1911. His father was Commander Harry Ross Hubbard of the United States Navy. His mother was Dora May Hubbard (nee Waterbury de Wolfe, a thoroughly educated woman, a rarity in her time!).

Ron spent many of his childhood years on a large cattle ranch in Montana. It was on this ranch that he had learned to read and write by the time he was 3 ½ years old.

L. Ron Hubbard found the life of a young rancher very enjoyable. Long days were spent riding, breaking broncos, hunting coyote and taking his first steps as an explorer.

For it was in Montana that he had his first encounter with another culture—the Blackfoot (Pikuni) Indians. He became a blood brother of the Pikuni and was later to write about them in his first published novel, *Buckskin Brigades*.

Before Ron was 10 years old, he had become very thoroughly educated both in schools as well as by his mother.

So it was that by the time he was 12 years old, L. Ron Hubbard had already read a large number of the world's greatest classics—and his interest in philosophy and religion was born.

Not that the explorer in him had been stilled. Far from it. A Montana newspaper of the period reported thusly on one of Helena's newest high school students:

Ronald Hubbard has the distinction of being the only boy in the country to secure an eagle scout badge at the age of 12 years. He was a Boy Scout in Washington, D.C., before coming to Helena.

In Washington, D.C., he had also become a close friend of President Coolidge's son, Calvin Jr., whose early death accelerated L. Ron Hubbard's interest in the mind and spirit of Man.

The following years, from 1925 to 1929, saw the young Mr. Hubbard, between the ages of 14 and 18, as a budding and enthusiastic world traveller and adventurer. His father was sent to the Far East and having the financial support of his wealthy grandfather, L. Ron Hubbard spent these years journeying throughout Asia.

He explored many out-of-the-way places and saw many strange-seeming peoples and customs. But it was in Northern China and India, while studying with holy men, that he became vitally engrossed in the subject of the spiritual destiny of Mankind.

With the death of his grandfather, the Hubbard

family returned to the United States, and, after intense study at Swavely Preparatory School in Manassas, Virginia and at Woodward Preparatory School in Washington, D.C., he enrolled at the George Washington University Engineering School in the fall of 1930.

At George Washington, L. Ron Hubbard became associate editor of the University newspaper *The Hatchet*, and was a member of many of the University's clubs and societies including the Twentieth Marine Corps Reserve, the George Washington College Company.

It was while at George Washington University that he learned to fly and discovered a particular aptitude as a glider pilot.

Here, also, he was enrolled in one of the first nuclear physics courses ever taught in an American university.

As a student, barely 20 years old, he supported himself by writing and within a very few years he already established himself as a professional photographer and technical article writer in aviation and sports magazines.

He made the time during these same busy college years to act as a director with the Caribbean Motion Picture Expedition of 1931.

In 1932, L. Ron Hubbard, age 21, achieved an ambitious 'first.' Conducting the West Indies Minerals Survey, he made the first complete mineralogical survey of Puerto Rico. This was pioneer exploration in the great tradition, opening up a predictable, accurate body of data for the benefit of others. Later, in other less materialistic fields, this was to be his way many, many times over.

In the 30s, he became an established writer and published his work in over 90 periodicals and magazines.

His aviation articles in *The Sportsman Pilot* dealing, among other things, with aerial navigation of the Indies, date from this period.

By 1936, at the age of 25, Hubbard was in Hollywood, ready for adventures of a different sort. Working as a scriptwriter on several films, he made his reputation there, appropriately enough, with the highly profitable Columbia production titled "The Secret of Treasure Island."

Hollywood has always been a good place to study "what makes men tick," and the late 30s were no exception. In fact, L. Ron Hubbard dates his own statement of the discovery of the primary law of life, summarily expressed by the command "Survive!" at 1938. He says, "A work was written at that time which embraced Man and his activities." This was the still-unpublished "Excalibur," a sensational volume which was a summation of life based on his analysis of the state of Mankind. The part played in this by his explorations, journeys and experiences in the four corners of the earth, amongst all kinds of men, was crucial.

As a logical consequence of his achievements in the field, L. Ron Hubbard on December 12th, 1939, not yet 30 years old, was proposed as a member of the Explorers Club of New York. He was duly elected a Member on February 19th, 1940. Now the honors were coming.

In May of the same year, 1940, he was awarded his first Explorers Club flag for conducting the Alaskan Radio Experimental Expedition. Carrying the Club's flag on an expedition is one of the highest honors granted.

He found time to take his sailing ship (a ketch) *Magician* which he called "Maggie," along the coasts of Alaska adding to the existing knowledge of unfrequented navigational passages and islands in America's northwest ocean waters.

Also in 1940, on 17th December, he earned his "License to Master of Steam and Motor Vessels" from the U.S. Department of Commerce. Within 4 ½ months he had further obtained a second certificate attesting to his marine skill: "License to Master of Sail Vessels" ("Any Ocean"), for the U.S. Navy Hydrographic Office.

In 1941, he was ordered to the Philippines (which he had known as a youngster) at the outbreak of World War II.

He survived the early war in the South Pacific. He

saw enough of war at first hand to be sickened by it. In 1944, crippled and blinded he found himself in Oak Knoll Naval Hospital. From Commander Thompson of the Medical Corps of the U.S. Navy, a friend of his father and a personal student of Sigmund Freud, he had received while still young an extensive education in the field of the human mind. He developed techniques that would help him overcome his injuries and regain his abilities.

Altogether, he spent nearly a year at Oak Knoll, during which time he synthesized what he had learned of Eastern philosophy, his understanding of nuclear physics and his experiences among men. He says, "I set out to find from nuclear physics and a knowledge of the physical universe, things entirely lacking in Asian philosophy."

He concluded that the results he was obtaining could help others toward greater ability and happiness, and it was during this period that some of the basic tenets of Dianetics and Scientology were first formulated.

By 1947 he recovered fully.

In 1948 he wrote *Dianetics: The Original Thesis*, his first formal report of his discoveries about the mind and life. The manuscript was copied out extensively and quickly passed from hand to hand in many countries.

A grass roots interest in Dianetics spread. Letters began to pour in asking for clarifications and advice.

Answering them was becoming a full time occupation.

What was needed was a complete popular text on the subject which would answer all questions. A publisher, Hermitage House, was anxious to print such a book. There was one condition: the manuscript had to be delivered in six weeks.

The book was written in six weeks.

This was the anatomy of the mind, and a technology called auditing. 180,000 words of breakthrough, *Dianetics: The Modern Science of Mental Health* exploded onto the booklists of May, 1950, like a roman candle of life and hope. Providing, as it did, for a truly workable school of the mind which would predictably improve the human condition, it leapt to the top of the *New York Times* best seller list and just stayed there.

Almost immediately, thousands of readers began to apply the data from the book and Dianetic groups sprang up across the country, with and without sanction.

Realizing already at this stage that the mind in itself, no matter how liberated, was limiting and that there was something 'animating' the mind, he permitted the founding in 1950, of the Hubbard Dianetic Research Foundation to facilitate investigation into the realm of the spirit. Thus was Scientology born.

The United States Government at this time attempted to monopolize all his researches and force him to work on a project "to make man more suggestible" and when he was unwilling, tried to blackmail him by ordering him back to active duty to perform this function. Having many friends he was able to instantly resign from the Navy and escape this trap. The Government never forgave him for this and soon began vicious, covert international attacks upon his work, all of which were proven false and baseless, which were to last 27 years and finally culminated in the Government being sued for 750 million dollars for conspiracy.

The pace of research and writing quickened. To an already crammed schedule, lectures were added. These lectures, usually arranged in a series spread across one or two weeks of intensive meetings, were later to become famous, and many are preserved on tape and in book form.

The Oakland Lecture Series in September of 1950 and the Los Angeles Lecture Series in late November of that same year are preserved in book form in *Notes on the Lectures*.

1951 saw the publication of *Self Analysis*, a very practical self-help volume giving a way to improve memory, reaction time and general ability.

Also in 1951, *Science of Survival* was published, a 506-page volume outlining and describing in detail the relationship of Man to the physical universe and an exact pattern for the prediction of human behavior.

In 1952, L. Ron Hubbard published *Scientology 8-80*, which described the physical manifestations of thought and past identities in terms of flows and ridges surrounding the body.

A new series of lectures was delivered in Philadelphia, also in 1952, in course format: The Philadelphia Doctorate Course. These lectures, all of which were preserved on tape and are available today, went into great detail about the behavioral patterns of the spirit—a breathtaking delineation of the spiritual landscape he was now surveying.

Many awards and honors were offered and conferred on L. Ron Hubbard. He did accept an honorary Doctor of Philosophy given in recognition of his outstanding work on Dianetics and "as an inspiration to the many people . . . who had been inspired by him to take up advanced studies in this field . . . ."

An historic milestone in the history of Dianetics and Scientology was passed in February, 1954, with the founding of the first Church of Scientology. This was in keeping with the religious nature of the tenets dating from the earliest days of research. It was obvious that he had been exploring religious territory right along. And whatever the name given to the technique or study and whatever way it had been interpreted by skeptics or sensation-mongers, it was apparent to those with a sense of history and Man's ages-old spiritual quest that this was indeed the realm of the soul and its havens.

And Dianetics and Scientology were snowballing across the United States and reaching other shores—England first of all. *Dianetics: The Modern Science of Mental Health* was everywhere. As early as 1951, the publisher Casini had brought out the first Italian edition in Rome.

In 1954, there was another lecture series, in Phoenix, Arizona. These were startling talks on the qualities and fundamental nature of all life. Today they can be studied in book form: *The Phoenix Lectures*. It was in this series that he described the Axioms of Scientology, those self-evident truths which provide the philosophical foundation for the entire religion.

And in 1955, the U.S. District Court for the District of Columbia certified that he was a Minister of the Church.

On November 13th, 1957, The International Oceanographic Foundation, with headquarters in Miami, Florida, made him a Fellow of the Society, "by virtue of contributions to the advancement and extension of knowledge and discovery in oceanography and the marine sciences."

At the end of the 50s, L. Ron Hubbard moved his home to Saint Hill Manor, a vast and beautiful Georgian residence in the green hills of Sussex, in England. Increasingly effective techniques had been developed for the further liberation of the spirit and the exploration he now conducted was leading inevitably to spiritual freedom, the ages-long quest of Man's greatest religious leaders.

On a literally 'down-to-earth' level, though, L. Ron Hubbard was moving in a direction new even for him. 1959 and 1960 saw him, now firmly established at Saint Hill, conducting a series of revolutionary experiments on plants in a fully equipped greenhouse laboratory on the Manor grounds. On September 25, 1959, a local paper was able to record that "L. Ron Hubbard . . . whose researches in plant life at the Manor look like revolutionizing horticulture, has carried out an experiment which points to the fact that plants react in much the same way to certain situations as do human beings."

His discoveries on the nature of life in plants were described by one journal as "25 years in advance of today's methods and ideas." This proved prophetic for 13 years subsequent to L. Ron Hubbard's findings, experiments on plant life reaction in Swiss, German, Russian, American, British and Canadian scientific institutions have validated his findings in rigorous test conditions.

In 1961 he set up an educational visit to teach the now standard methods of Dianetics and Scientology, to ensure uniform quality of application. Students came from all over the world. And over the next few years returned to their local Academies to use study methods which revolutionized the philosophy of education.

151

Student failures could be recovered. Study barriers by 1965 had been overcome.

For more than two millenia Man had dreamed of a spiritual state where, free of his own mental aberrations, he would be truly himself. L. Ron Hubbard called this state "Clear." And, at Saint Hill, in August of 1965, he announced the attainment of Clear.

The dream of Buddha, attained by the few, was a reality, Man could be Clear.

And the reality which was and is Clear was to be available to all who followed the exact route he had laid out. This route he called The Bridge. For it was as a span across the abyss of misery and degradation and sorrow to a higher plateau of ability and happiness.

In 1966, having paved the way to Clear so that it was safe and sure for others to walk, the Founder resigned from any official administrative capacity in Scientology.

He discovered and developed the astonishing materials above Clear now known as the Advanced Courses. These are the eight OT Sections, enabling one who has attained Clear to regain abilities never before accurately credited to the human spirit, as an Operating Thetan, a spiritual being operating independently of the laws of the physical universe.

In July of 1966, OT I and OT II were released and, during the last months of 1967, came the breakthrough of OT III.

A research accomplishment of immense magnitude, OT III has been called "The Wall of Fire." Here are contained the secrets of a disaster which resulted in the decay of life as we know it in this sector of the galaxy. The end result of OT III is truly the stuff of which dreams are spun: The return of full self-determinism and complete freedom from overwhelm.

The formation of a new Scientology group dates from this same period. Hearing of L. Ron Hubbard's plans for further exploration and research into, among other things, past civilizations, many Scientologists wanted to join him and help. They adopted the name "Sea Organization."

January, 1968, saw the release of OT Sections IV, V and VI as a sequence of spiritual abilities to be reached. In September of 1970 came OT VII, and in 1978 L. Ron Hubbard released OT VIII.

These OT Sections and the abilities and awarenesses they restore to the individual are the greatest gifts to Man of an honest man who has retained 'his common touch' and humility.

People all over the world consider that they have no truer friend.

Glossary

Aberration, a departure from rational thought or behavior. From the Latin, *aberrare*, to wander from; Latin, *ab*, away, *errare*, to wander. It means basically to err, to make mistakes, or more specifically to have fixed ideas which are not true. The word is also used in its scientific sense. It means departure from a straight line. If a line should go from A to B, then if it is "aberrated" it would go from A to some other point, to some other point, to some other point, to some other point, to some other point and finally arrive at B. Taken in its scientific sense, it would also mean the lack of straightness or to see crookedly as, in example, a man sees a horse but thinks he sees an elephant. Aberrated conduct would be wrong conduct, or conduct not supported by reason.

AOSH DK, Advanced Organization—Saint Hill, Denmark. A Scientology organization in Denmark which delivers advanced courses in Scientology.

Auditing, same as processing.

Auditor, Scientology processing is done on the

154

principle of making an individual look at his own existence, and improve his ability to confront what he is and where he is. An auditor is the person trained in the technology and whose job it is to ask the person to look, and get him to do so. The word auditor is used because it means one who listens, and a Scientology auditor does listen.

Close Terminals, the greatest ability of thought is DIFFERENTIATION. So long as one can differentiate, one is sane. Its opposite is IDENTIFICATION. When one begins to identify, one has "closed terminals" too closely, and believes one terminal is another terminal.

Dianetics, a system of coordinated axioms which resolve problems concerning human behavior and psychosomatic illnesses.

E-Meter, Hubbard Electrometer. An electronic instrument for measuring mental state and change of state in individuals, as an aid to precision and speed in auditing. The E-Meter is not intended or effective for the diagnosis, treatment or prevention of any disease.

Genetic Blueprint, the plans of construction of a new body in the orthodox manner of conception, birth and growth.

Grant Beingness, the ability to assume or grant (give, allow) beingness is probably the highest of human virtues. It is even more important to be able to permit (allow) other people to have beingness than to be able oneself to assume it.

Group Auditing, the application of certain Scientology processes to a group of people by a trained practitioner.

No-Game Condition, life is a game. A game consists of freedom, barriers and purposes. This is a scientific fact, not merely an observation. Freedom exists amongst barriers. A totality of barriers and a totality of freedom alike are no-game conditions. Each is similarly cruel. Each is similarly purposeless.

Postulate, a self-created truth would be simply the consideration generated by self. Well, we just borrow the word which is in seldom use in the English language, we call that postulate. And we mean by postulate, self-created truth. He posts something. He puts something up and that's what a postulate is.

Processes, Scientology is employed by an auditor (a Scientology practitioner) upon individuals or small or large groups of people, in their presence. The auditor makes these people, at their choice, do various exercises, and these exercises (processes) bring about changes for the better in intelligence, behavior and general competence.

Processing, the principle of making an individual look at his own existence, and improve his ability to confront what he is and where he is.

Restimulation, the reactivation of a past memory due to similar circumstances in the present approximating circumstances of the past.

Run Out, erase.

Scientology, the term *SCIENTOLOGY* is taken from *scio* (knowing in the fullest meaning of the word) and *ology* (to study). It is an applied religious philosophy dealing with the study of knowledge, which through the application of its technology, can bring about desirable changes in the conditions of life. Scientology, used by the trained and relatively untrained person, improves the intelligence, ability, behavior, skill and appearance of people.

BUY THESE
DIANETICS AND SCIENTOLOGY BOOKS
BY L. RON HUBBARD

Dianetics: The Original Thesis

Written two years before public release of the discoveries of Dianetics. $7.00

Dianetics: The Evolution of a Science

L. Ron Hubbard's exciting story of the first quarter century of Dianetic research. $6.00

Dianetics: The Modern Science of Mental Health

A spectacular international best seller from the moment of its publication in May, 1950, this is *the* book of Man's most advanced knowledge and technology in the field of the human mind. $10.00

Self Analysis

A simple self-help volume of tests and processes based on the discoveries contained in Dianetics. $7.00

How to Live Though an Executive

A must for any executive or anyone who works near one. Hundreds of applications in every phase of life. L. Ron Hubbard's earliest work on the subject of organization. $7.00

Scientology: The Fundamentals of Thought

Basic book of the theory and practice of Scientology for beginners. $6.00

The Problems of Work

Scientology applied to the workaday world. $6.00

Have You Lived Before This Life?

When Dianetics touched off the Bridey Murphey craze, conservative investigators were justifiably upset. Now quite conservative, trained Scientologists have tested a series of seventy cases. Their fascinating findings are given in this book. $8.95

Scientology: A New Slant on Life

A collection of all-time favorite essays by the Founder of Scientology. $7.00

The Basic Scientology Picture Book Volume 1

A visual aid to a better understanding of Man and the material universe. $4.50

The Basic Dianetics Picture Book

A visual aid for a quicker understanding and dissemination of Standard Dianetics and Dianetic Pastoral Counseling.

$3.00

Available from:

SCIENTOLOGY PUBLICATIONS ORGANIZATION
4833 Fountain Avenue, East Annex
Los Angeles, California 90029

or the bookstore of your nearest Church of Scientology (see Churches address list on following pages.)

FREE MEMBERSHIPS

You may have a FREE six-month Membership by writing to the Membership Officer of your local Organization. In addition to a discount on books, tape lectures and many other items, you also receive free magazines with vital data, Scientology news and technical information. Discount privileges are allowed on orders sent with membership application.

DISCOUNT

10% for International Church of Scientology members.

Contact Your Nearest Church

**Flag Land Base
Advanced Organizations
Saint Hill Organizations**

UNITED STATES
OF AMERICA

Church of Scientology of California
Flag Service Organization
210 South Fort Harrison Avenue
Clearwater, Florida 33516

Church of Scientology of California
Advanced Organization Los Angeles
1306 North Berendo Street
Los Angeles, California 90027

Church of Scientology of California
American Saint Hill Organization
1413 North Berendo Street
Los Angeles, California 90027

Church of Scientology of California
American Saint Hill Foundation
1413 North Berendo Street
Los Angeles, California 90027

UNITED
KINGDOM

Hubbard College of Scientology
Advanced Organization Saint Hill
Saint Hill Manor, East Grinstead
Sussex, England, RH 19 4JY

EUROPE

Church of Scientology
Advanced Organization Europe
Jernbanegade 6
1608 Copenhagen V, Denmark

Church of Scientology
Saint Hill Organization Europe
Jernbanegade 6
1608 Copenhagen V, Denmark

Church of Scientology
Publications Organization Denmark
Jernbanegade 6
1608 Copenhagen V, Denmark

Churches

WESTERN
UNITED STATES

Church of Scientology Austin
2804 Rio Grande
Austin
Texas 78705

Church of Scientology Austin
  Foundation
2804 Rio Grande
Austin
Texas 78705

Church of Scientology Denver
1640 Welton
Denver
Colorado 80202

Church of Scientology Hawaii
143 Nenue Street
Honolulu
Hawaii 96821

Church of Scientology Hawaii
  Foundation
143 Nenue Street
Honolulu, Hawaii 96821

Church of Scientology Las Vegas
2108 Industrial Road
Las Vegas
Nevada 89102

Church of Scientology Las Vegas
  Foundation
2108 Industrial Road
Las Vegas, Nevada 89102

Church of Scientology Los Angeles
1415 North Berendo Street
Los Angeles
California 90027

Church of Scientology Los Angeles
  Foundation
1415 North Berendo Street
Los Angeles
California 90027

Church of Scientology Portland
333 South West Park Avenue
Portland
Oregon 97205

Church of Scientology Portland
  Foundation
333 South West Park Avenue
Portland
Oregon 97205

Church of Scientology Sacramento
819 19th Street
Sacramento
California 95814

Church of Scientology Sacramento
  Foundation
819 19th Street
Sacramento, California 95814

Church of Scientology San Diego
926 "C" Street
San Diego
California 92101

Church of Scientology San Diego
  Foundation
926 "C" Street
San Diego, California 92101

Church of Scientology San Francisco
414 Mason Street, Room 400
San Francisco
California 94102

Church of Scientology San Francisco
  Foundation
414 Mason Street, Room 400
San Francisco, California 94102

Church of Scientology Seattle
1531 4th Avenue
Seattle
Washington 98101

Church of Scientology Seattle
  Foundation
1531 4th Avenue
Seattle
Washington 98101

Church of Scientology St. Louis
3730 Lindell Boulevard
St. Louis
Missouri 63108

Church of Scientology St. Louis
  Foundation
3730 Lindell Boulevard
St. Louis, Missouri 63108

Church of Scientology Twin Cities
730 Hennepin Avenue
Minneapolis
Minnesota 55403

Church of Scientology Twin Cities
  Foundation
730 Hennepin Avenue
Minneapolis
Minnesota 55403

EASTERN
UNITED STATES

Church of Scientology Boston
448 Beacon Street
Boston
Massachusetts 02215

Church of Scientology Boston
  Foundation
448 Beacon Street
Boston
Massachusetts 02215

Church of Scientology Buffalo
1116 Elmwood Avenue
Buffalo
New York 14222

Church of Scientology Buffalo
  Foundation
1116 Elmwood Avenue
Buffalo
New York 14222

Church of Scientology Chicago
1555 Maple Street
Evanston
Illinois 60201

Church of Scientology Chicago
  Foundation
1555 Maple Street
Evanston
Illinois 60201

Church of Scientology Detroit
3905 Rochester Road
Royal Oak
Michigan 48073

Church of Scientology Detroit
  Foundation
3905 Rochester Road
Royal Oak
Michigan 48073

Church of Scientology Miami
120 Giralda
Coral Gables
Florida 33134

Church of Scientology Miami
  Foundation
120 Giralda
Coral Gables
Florida 33134

Church of Scientology New York
28-30 West 74th Street
New York
New York 10023

Church of Scientology New York
  Foundation
28-30 West 74th Street
New York
New York 10023

Church of Scientology Philadelphia
8 West Lancaster Avenue
Ardmore
Pennsylvania 19003

Church of Scientology Philadelphia
  Foundation
8 West Lancaster Avenue
Ardmore
Pennsylvania 19003

Founding Church of Scientology
  of Washington, D.C.
2125 South Street, N.W.
Washington
D.C. 20008

Church of Scientology
Washington D.C. Foundation
2125 South Street, N. W.
Washington
D.C. 20008